G. Schirmer's Collection of Operas

BALFE

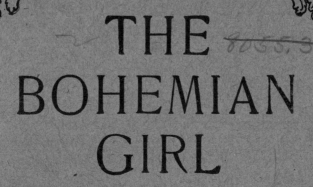

THE BOHEMIAN GIRL

G. SCHIRMER · NEW YORK

1808—1870.

G. SCHIRMER'S
COLLECTION
OF
OPERAS.

THE BOHEMIAN GIRL

AN OPERA IN THREE ACTS

BY

MICHAEL WILLIAM BALFE

THE LIBRETTO BY

ALFRED BUNN

THE MUSIC REVISED BY

MAX SPICKER

WITH A CRITICAL AND HISTORICAL ESSAY BY

RICHARD ALDRICH

G. SCHIRMER ~ NEW YORK.

THE BOHEMIAN GIRL

Characters of the Drama

COUNT ARNHEIM, Governor of Presburg . . . . Baritone

THADDEUS, a proscribed Pole . . . . Tenor

FLORESTEIN, nephew of the Count . . . . Tenor

DEVILSHOOF, Chief of the Gipsies . . . . Bass

CAPTAIN OF THE GUARD . . . . Bass

AN OFFICER . . . . Tenor

ARLINE, daughter of the Count . . . . Soprano

BUDA, her attendant . . . . Soprano

QUEEN OF THE GIPSIES . . . . Soprano

Chorus of Gipsies, Huntsmen, Guests, etc.

THE SCENE IS LAID IN PRESBURG AND ENVIRONS

16118

THE BOHEMIAN GIRL

Grand Opera in Three Acts

Words by ALFRED BUNN

Music by
MICHAEL WILLIAM BALFE

First Performed at Her Majesty's Theatre, Drury Lane, London, November 27, 1843, with the Following Cast:

ARLINE, ...	Soprano, ...	MISS ROMER
GIPSY QUEEN, ...	Contralto, ...	MISS BETTS
THADDEUS, ...	Tenor, ...	MR. HARRISON
DEVILSHOOF, ...	Bass, ...	MR. STRETTON
COUNT ARNHEIM, . . .	Bass, ...	MR. BORRANI
FLORESTEIN, ...	Tenor, ...	MR. DURNSET

The Bohemian Girl

There seems to be a hopeless disagreement between the critics and the public as to " The Bohemian Girl." Few operas have been so generally faulted, both by the reviewers for the press at the time of its production and by more deliberate critical writers since; yet not many English operas have had a greater measure of success, as success is measured—by popularity. After the lapse of near sixty years, Balfe's work is still one of the indispensable resources of the manager who wishes to give English opera, and its title is one to conjure with. It may not live to reach the span of a century—to which, as has been truly observed, only a very few masterworks of the greatest geniuses have ever attained—and, indeed, it has long been a stranger to the aristocratic opera houses of the world's capitals. But that it has survived nearly two generations of opera-goers, and still keeps its place in the hearts of a great section of the public, are facts that must be reckoned with as denoting a vitality not given to many works of its class. Balfe was no great musician; he had not even the instinct for dramatic music, nor much artistic conscience; but he had a remarkable fund of invention

v

16118

of a certain sort, the practical knowledge of writing fluently for the voice, and the power of producing melodies of the kind that fasten themselves deep in the popular heart.

To trace the origin of "The Bohemian Girl" leads us far back into the literary history of Europe. Balfe's libretto was devised by Alfred Bunn, the erratic London operatic manager, who learned through his ventures with English and Italian opera more ways of spelling ruin than it falls to the lot of most, even of his profession, to learn. He was the author of a number of librettos for English operas, produced in London during the period of his activity there, deriving his inspiration almost altogether from French models. This was the case with "The Bohemian Girl." Its theme was taken directly from the French ballet, "La Gipsy," produced in Paris in 1839, and constructed by the Marquis de Saint-Georges, first of French librettists after Scribe, and collaborator with many of the French composers of the day — in this instance with three, Benoist, Ambroise Thomas and Marliani. According to Mr. Sutherland Edwards, however, "The Bohemian Girl" is not only identical in subject with "La Gipsy," but is a translation of an unpublished opera founded on that ballet, and written also by the Marquis de Saint-Georges. The English version is evidently called "The Bohemian Girl" because the Marquis de Saint-Georges entitled his "La Bohémienne," which means "The Gipsy Girl," and has nothing to do with Bohemia, either the country or that strange section of society that has appropriated its name. Mr. Bunn seems to have mistaken the meaning of the title, and having suggested several others (including "Thaddeus of Warsaw," which was obviously misleading, through its connection with a once popular novel upon an entirely different subject), settled upon "The Bohemian Girl," as being an exact translation, though the heroine of his story is not a Bohemian, and Bohemia is in no way suggested in it. For his ballet as well as his opera, M. de Saint-Georges had gone to Cervantes. The Spanish master published his "Novelas Exemplares" in 1613, some years after his great masterpiece, "Don Quixote." These, says one of his biographers, are a collection of tales of very various character, which are the true originals, in the modern literature of Europe, of the novel or story of real life, with plot, scenery, character and local color. "In the charming story of 'La Gitanilla' is to be found the germ of all the Gipsy romances, poems and operas that have since delighted the world." Of these last there are indeed many; though we need mention now only the play, "Preciosa," to which Weber wrote an overture and some incidental music. This was derived directly from the same story by Cervantes that has furnished the substance of "The Bohemian Girl."

That the story underwent much modification before it reached the stage as an English opera, may easily be imagined. Preciosa, in Cervantes' "exemplary novel," "La Gitanilla" ("The Gipsy Girl"), is a member of a Gipsy band and is under the special charge of an alleged aunt. Don Juan, a young nobleman of Madrid, falls so violently in love with the girl that he gives up his family and joins the band of Gipsies as her affianced husband. In the course of their travels a young woman of the country becomes enamored of Don Juan and wishes to marry him, but being repulsed, accuses him of theft,

VI

having previously put a number of her jewels with his belongings. The evidence being thus against him, he is imprisoned; and having struck down a soldier of the guard, who insults him, is charged with murder. Preciosa goes to the house of the governor of the province to intercede for him. The Gipsy aunt, seeing no other way to extricate Don Juan, also repairs thither with a casket of jewels as proof of the revelation which she then makes, that Preciosa is the governor's daughter. A birthmark upon the girl's shoulder and a peculiar web between two of her toes complete the identification. She refuses, however, to give up Don Juan; and when the latter proves his noble birth and his true rank, their marriage takes place.

The incidents of Balfe's opera are supposed to occur in Hungary. Preparations for a hunt are in progress upon the grounds of Count Arnheim, governor of Presburg. The Count, with his daughter, Arline, and his effeminate nephew, Florestein, depart upon this errand, when Thaddeus, a Polish exile and fugitive, appears, in flight from the Austrian soldiers. Then comes a troop of Gipsies, headed by Devilshoof, who hears Thaddeus's story and induces him to join them. At this juncture Florestein and some of the hunters return in quest of Arline, who has been attacked by a stag. It falls to Thaddeus to rescue her, whereupon he is overwhelmed by the gratitude of the Count and invited to join the festivities that are to ensue. At the banquet he refuses to toast the Austrian Emperor, and the guests are about to seize him, when Devilshoof interferes, and is arrested instead. Thaddeus departs, and the Gipsy immediately escapes, taking Arline with him.

Twelve years now elapse, during which the Count has given up his daughter for lost. She has been living with the Gipsies, of whose band Thaddeus has also become a member. Their camp in a street of Presburg is disclosed in the second act. Waiting in quest of plunder under the lead of Devilshoof, the Gipsies capture a prisoner who is none other than Count Arnheim's nephew, Florestein. He is despoiled of his jewelry, including a medallion, which is appropriated by Devilshoof. They again disappear, and Arline, who has been asleep during this episode, awakes, to tell Thaddeus, who has been watching her, of her dream, in the aria, "I Dreamt that I Dwelt in Marble Halls." Thaddeus then discloses to her the fact that the scar on her arm was inflicted by the stag from which he rescued her ; but he does not enlighten her as to her birth and family. He declares his love for her, and is then and there united to her, in accordance with the customs of the tribe, by the Gipsy Queen, who appears at this moment. She, however, vows vengeance secretly upon the pair as she performs the rite, for she is herself in love with Thaddeus. The scene changes, and we see the Gipsy band as a part of the throng at a fair in the streets of Presburg. Florestein also makes his appearance in the crowd, and, being taken by the appearance of Arline, addresses her, which she vigorously resents. The Queen, recognizing in Florestein the owner of the medallion, gives it to Arline, ostensibly to reward her for her spirit, really with the purpose of brewing trouble. The trouble comes when Florestein sees the trinket upon Arline's neck, and charges her with its theft. In defending her Thaddeus is arrested with her. Again the scene changes. Count Arnheim is in his apartment in the Hall of Justice, and gives utterance to his grief at the loss of his daughter in the aria, "The Heart Bowed Down with Weight of Woe." Arline is brought before him for trial. He sees the scar on her arm and asks its origin. Arline repeats the story Thaddeus has recently told her, whereupon the Count recognizes her as his lost daughter.

In the third act Arline is found restored to her father's home, but still true to her love for Thaddeus. Her lover comes to her for an interview, with the aid and companionship of Devilshoof, and tells her again of his love in the song, "When Other Lips and Other Hearts." They are interrupted by the approach of a large company of guests; Thaddeus conceals himself, and Devilshoof escapes. In the midst of the festivities the Gipsy Queen arrives, closely veiled for disguise, and reveals the presence of Thaddeus. He is dragged forth from his hiding-place and ordered to leave the house. Arline declares her love for him, proclaims her purpose to follow him, and implores her father to relent. Thaddeus proudly claims equality with the Count, through his noble Polish ancestry, which he celebrates in the song "When the Fair Land of Poland." The Count yields and gives his daughter to Thaddeus. The Queen, transported with jealous rage, causes one of the Gipsies to fire at him as he is embracing Arline, but Devilshoof is at hand, and, seizing the weapon, averts the bullet from Thaddeus. It kills the Queen instead. At this opportune moment the curtain falls.

With all the change of surroundings and of incident, the few fundamental elements of the story of "The Bohemian Girl" are easily traced in Cervantes' tale.

In 1841, Balfe, who had already composed a number of operas for the London stage, undertook the duties of a manager, with the purpose of establishing English opera in the capital. For this he wrote and produced, with his wife in the leading rôle, the opera "Keolanthe," and had already made considerable progress on the music of "The Bohemian Girl." The operatic enterprise, however, came to an abrupt end within a few weeks, and Balfe, seeing better prospects in Paris, betook himself thither, having deposited the manuscript of his unfinished opera with a London music publisher. The promises of Paris were realized, and Balfe had the honor of being called upon by the mighty Scribe to furnish the music to a French opera, "Le Puits d'Amour." For this he appears to have used several of the pieces originally incorporated into "The Bohemian Girl." At all events, when he returned to London, in 1843, he recurred to this work, and revised it thoroughly, adding several new numbers to take the place of those used for the French opera. Bunn, after one of his periodical bankruptcies, had returned again to Her Majesty's Theatre, Drury Lane, as its manager. He wanted an English opera, and found what he wanted in "The Bohemian Girl," for which he himself had written the book a few years before. The production took place on November 27, 1843, under the musical direction of Julius Benedict. Its success was immediate, though, as we have intimated, the newspaper critics did not hesitate to point out its defects upon both the musical and dramatic sides.

VIII

16118

The fame of "The Bohemian Girl" soon spread to other countries. The first city to hear it outside of London was New York, in 1844. Mr. and Mrs. Edward Seguin had been singing in this city for a number of years, beginning their long and honorable participation in the early operatic history of the United States. They returned from a visit to England in the autumn of 1844 with a score of Balfe's new work, and brought it out at the Park Theatre—then the principal playhouse of the metropolis—on November 25. The performance, which was under the musical direction of Mr. Chubb, was given with the following cast:

ARLINE (Act 1), ... MISS DYOTT
ARLINE (Acts 2 and 3), ... MRS. SEGUIN
GIPSY QUEEN, ... MRS. KNIGHT
THADDEUS, ... MR. FRAZER
DEVILSHOOF, ... MR. SEGUIN
COUNT ARNHEIM, ... MR. A. ANDREWS
FLORESTEIN, ... MR. S. PEARSON

No explanation is given in the contemporary records of the division of the part of Arline between two singers. The production was "the operatic success of the period," according to Mr. Richard Grant White, quite eclipsing the Italian opera that was in progress at Palmo's Theatre in Chambers Street. The whole town fell to singing, whistling and grinding on the barrel-organ the principal airs from it. It soon reached Germany, and performances of it were given in Hamburg, under the title of "La Gitana," and in other cities. In 1850 it was produced in Vienna as "Die Zigeunerin," by a M. Pokorny, at a new theatre, the Wieden. The next year Balfe himself was invited thither to conduct a performance of his opera, which took place with much enthusiasm; Staudigl, the famous basso, being in the cast. In 1858, an Italian version of the work, under the title of "La Zingara," was brought out at Drury Lane, in London, with Piccolomini in the cast as Arline, and Alboni as the Gipsy Queen. According to Henry F. Chorley, it "was received with a triumph which had never been exceeded even in the days of the Catalani;" with "applause from the many loud enough to rend the heavens." For the spoken dialogue recitative was substituted in the Italian version, as was the case in the French, eleven years later. This was given at the Théâtre Lyrique in Paris, with the title of "La Bohémienne," on December 30, 1869, under the direction of Pasdeloup. The translation was by the inevitable Marquis de Saint-Georges, who recast and extended the opera to five acts, while Balfe wrote several additional numbers for it. The cast included MM. Montjauze, Lutz and Becquié, and Mlles. Wertheimber, and Brunet Lafleur. Here, too, the opera made a great popular success. Balfe, who was in Paris to superintend the production, was a hero of the hour; he received the cross of the Legion of Honor from Napoleon III., and was made Commander of the Order of Carlos III. by the Regent of Spain.

RICHARD ALDRICH

NEW YORK, June 9, 1902.

IX

THE BOHEMIAN GIRL

ACT I.

SCENE I.

The château and grounds of COUNT ARNHEIM, *on the Danube, near Presburg. On one side, the principal entrance to the castle ; opposite is a statue of the Emperor, above which a party is employed raising the Austrian flag.*

[*On the rising of the curtain, the Retainers of* COUNT ARNHEIM *are discovered preparing for the chase.*

CHORUS.

Up with the banner, and down with
    the slave
  Who shall dare to dispute the right,
Wherever its folds in their glory wave,
  Of the Austrian Eagle's flight ;
     Its pinion flies
     Free in the skies,
    As that of the airy king,
     Thro' danger fleets
     As heart that beats
    Beneath his pluméd wing.

[*After they have fixed the flag they all come forward.*

Now the foeman lies low, and the
    battle-field's won,
We may honor in peace what in war
    we have done.
    The stirring chase, the festive
     board,
    The varied charms which each
     afford,
     Shall day and night beguile ;
    And care shall be drowned in that
     glass
    Which nothing on earth can sur-
     pass
    But a lovely woman's smile.

Then up with the banner, &c.

[*At the end of the Chorus,* COUNT ARNHEIM *and* FLORESTEIN *enter from château* (S.E.L.), *followed by various neighboring Nobles, Pages, Huntsmen, &c., and his child,* ARLINE, *attended by* BUDA, *&c.*

SOLO.

COUNT.

A soldier's life
Has seen of strife
In all its forms so much,
That no gentler theme
The world will deem
A soldier's heart can touch.

CHORUS.

HUNTERS.

Away to the hill and glen,
Where the hunter's belted men
With bugles shake the air.

CHORUS.

RETAINERS.

Hail to the lord of our soil !
Hail ! hail !

[*The* COUNT, *after bowing to his friends, sees* ARLINE *and takes her in his arms.*

Cou.—Ah ! who can tell, save he who
    feels
    The care a parent's love re-
     veals,
     How dear, fond thing, thou
     art
    To this lone, widow'd heart !

Cho.—Away to the hill and glen, &c.

[During this, a Retainer brings down (R.) a rifle to FLORESTEIN, who puts it away from him. COUNT ARNHEIM exit into château. Nobles and Hunters ascend rocks and exeunt. ARLINE petitions BUDA to let her accompany them, and goes off by a footpath, at side of rocks, with her and FLORESTEIN.

[Enter THADDEUS, breathless and exhausted, in a state of great alarm.

THA.—A guard of Austrian soldiers are on my track, and I can no longer elude their vigilance. An exile from my wretched country, now a prey to the inveterate invader, my only hope is in some friendly shelter. (*Sees the statue of the Emperor.*) Ah! that tells me I am here on the very threshold of our enemies!

RECITATIVE.

THADDEUS.

Without friends, and without a home, my country, too! yes, I'm exiled from thee! What fate awaits me here, now? Pity, Heav'n! oh, calm my despair!

CAVATINA.

'Tis sad to leave our fatherland,
    And friends we there loved well,
To wander on a stranger strand,
    Where friends but seldom dwell.
Yet, hard as are such ills to bear,
    And deeply though they smart,
Their pangs are light to those who are
    The orphans of the heart!

Oh, if there were one gentle eye
    To weep when I might grieve,
One bosom to receive the sigh
    Which sorrow oft will heave;
One heart the ways of life to cheer,
    Though rugged they might be,
No language can express how dear
    That heart would be to me!

[At the end of song, a troop of Gipsies, headed by DEVILSHOOF, their leader, suddenly appear (R.), and are about to seize and rob THADDEUS; but presuming by his dress that he is a soldier, they stop and examine him.

CHORUS.

In the Gipsy's life you read
    The life that all would like to lead.
Sometimes under roof and sometimes
        thrown
    Where the wild wolf makes his lair;
For he who's no home to call his own
    Will find a home somewhere.

'Tis the maxim bold of man,
    What's another's prize to claim;
Then to keep all he can:
    We Gipsies do the same!
Thus a habit once, 'tis custom grown,
    Every man will take care,
If he has no home to call his own,
    To find a home somewhere.

THA.—The sight of these wanderers has inspired me with a project. (*To DEV.*) Your manner and habit please me. I should like to join your band. I am young, strong, and have, I hope, plenty of courage.

DEV.—Who are you?

THA.—One without money, without home, and without hope.

DEV.—You're just the fellow for us, then!

GIP. (*who is on the lookout on rock, R.*).—Soldiers are coming this way.

THA.—'Tis I they are in search of·

DEV.—Indeed! then they'll be cunning if they find you.

[In a moment they strip the soldier's dress off THADDEUS, and as they are putting on a Gipsy's frock, &c., over him, a roll of parchment, with seal attached, falls at the feet of DEVILSHOOF, who seizes it.

DEV.—What's this?

THA.—My commission! It is the only thing I possess on earth, and I will never part with it.

[Snatches it, conceals it in his bosom, and has just time to mix himself with the Gipsies, when a body of the Emperor's soldiers enter in pursuit.

OFF. (*scrutinizing Gipsies*).—Have you seen anyone pass this way—any stranger?

XII

Dev.—No one—stay—yes; a young Polish soldier ran by just now, and passed up those rocks.

Off.—That's he—thanks, friend!—Forward ! [*Exeunt soldiers up rocks.*

DUET AND CHORUS.

Dev.—Comrade, your hand,
    We understand
      Each other in a breath.
             [*Shaking his hand.*
    This grasp secures
    Its owner yours,
      In life, and until death.

Tha.—The scenes and days to me,
    Which seemed so blest to be,
      No time can e'er restore.

Cho.—In the Gipsy's life you read, &c.

Tha.—My wants are few—

Dev.—Want we ne'er knew,
      But what we could supply.

Tha.—Then, what is worse,
    I have no purse !

Dev.—We nothing have to buy.

Tha.—My heart 'twill wring—

Dev.—That is a thing
      In which we never deal.

Tha.—But all I need—

Dev.—'Twere best indeed
      To borrow, beg, or steal.

Cho —In the Gipsy's life you read, &c.

Dev.—Then rest you here while
      we explore
      What luck there is in store.

Tha.—The scenes and days to me,
    Which seemed so blest to
      be,
    No time can e'er restore.

Ensemble.

Cho —In the Gipsy's life you read, &c.

[*All exeunt R.—Loud shouts and alarms are heard, which become more and more distinct, when a body of Huntsmen are seen to cross the tree over the rocks, &c., and exeunt by the path where* Arline, *&c., went off. Alarms continue, when* Florestein *rushes in, apparently frightened to death.*

SONG.

Flo.—Is no succor near at hand ?
    For my intellect so reels,
  I am doubtful if I stand
    On my head or on my heels.
No gentleman, it's very clear,
    Such a shock should ever
      know,
And when once I become a peer,
    They shall not treat me so !

Then let every vassal arm,
    For my thanks he well
      deserves,
Who from this state of alarm
    Will protect my shattered
      nerves !
To think that one unused to fear
    Such a fright should ever
      know !
And when once I become a peer,
    They shall not treat me so !

[*At end of song,* Thaddeus *and Peasantry rush in, evincing the greatest alarm and terror.*

Tha.—What means this alarm ?

Pea.—The Count's child ~~and her attendant~~ have been attacked by an infuriated animal, and are probably killed ere this !

Tha.—What do I hear ?

[*He perceives the rifle that* Florestein *has left on the stage, utters an exclamation, seizes it, runs up the rocks, aims, fires, and instantly rushes off. The discharge of the rifle, and the alarm of the Peasantry, bring* Count Arnheim *and his party to the spot.* Devilshoof *enters at one side at the same time, watching.*

Cou.—Whence proceed these sounds of fear, and where is my darling child ?

[*All maintain a painful silence, when* Thaddeus *is seen rushing in, conveying* Arline, *who is wounded in the arm, and seems faint.*

Bud. (*falling at the* Count's *feet*).—We were pursued by the wild deer they were chasing, and but for the bravery of this young man (*pointing to* Tha.) the life of your child would have been sacrificed.

XIII

Cou. (*clasping his child in his arms*).—Praised be Providence! her life is saved, for she is all that renders mine happy (*Looking at her arm, then addressing* Buda.) Let her wound have every attention, though it presents no sign of danger.

[Buda *goes into the castle with* Arline, *and* Count Arnheim *advances to* Thaddeus.

Stranger, accept the hand of one who, however different from you in station, can never sufficiently thank you for the services you have rendered him.

Dev. (*aside*).—First to serve, and then be thanked by the persecutor of his country. The fellow's mad!

Cou.—I trust you will remain, and join the festivities we are about to indulge in; and 'twill gratify me to hear how I can be useful to you.

Tha.—I thank your lordship; but—

Cou. (*to the Nobles*). — Pray, my friends, join your entreaties to mine.

[Here *the Nobles all surround the* Count *and* Thaddeus, *and* Florestein, *coming up to him, says*—

Flo.—I'm extremely obliged to you for not shooting me as well as my little cousin—and I beg you'll—aw—stay—(*aside*)—A very common sort of personage, apparently.

Tha. (*to the* Count).—Be it as your lordship wishes.

Cou.—Then be seated, friends, and let the fête begin.

[*They all seat themselves at the tables, which have previously been laid on the* O.P. *opposite the castle.* Thaddeus *takes his seat at the farther end,* Florestein *occupying a prominent position. When they are seated, a variety of dances are introduced, during which* Buda *is seen at one of the windows, holding on her knee the child, whose arm is bound up. At the termination of the dancing the* Count *rises.*

Cou.—I ask you to pledge but once, and that is to the health and long life of your Emperor.

[Here *the Guests fill their glasses, rise, and turning towards the statue of the Emperor, drink, while the Peasantry surround it respectfully.* Thaddeus *alone keeps his seat, on perceiving which,* Florestein *goes up to the* Count, *and points it out to him.*

Flo.—Your new acquaintance, my dear uncle, is not overburdened with politeness or loyalty, for he neither fills his glass nor fulfils your wishes.

Cou. (*filling a glass, and going up to* Thaddeus).—I challenge you to empty this to the health of our Emperor.

Tha. (*taking the glass*).—I accept the challenge, and thus I empty the goblet.

[*Goes up to the statue and throws down the glass with the utmost contempt. A general burst of indignation follows.*

CHORUS OF GUESTS.

Who rise, draw their swords, and rush towards Thaddeus.

Down with the daring slave
Who disputes the right
Of a people's delight,
And would their anger brave!

Cou. (*To the Nobles and Guests, interposing between them and* Thaddeus),—

Although 'tis vain to mask
The rage such act demands,
Forgive me if I ask
His pardon at your hands;
If from your wrath I venture to have craved
The life of one, my more than life who saved.

(*To* Tha.)—Stranger, I answer not
One moment for your life;
Quit, while you may, a spot
Where you have raised a strife.
Your longer presence will more excite,
And this will the service you did me requite!

XIV

[*Throws* THADDEUS *a purse of gold.*
DEVILSHOOF *rushes in.*

DEV.—Where's the hand will dare to
    touch
    One hair of him I prize so much!
    [*Taking the hand of* THADDEUS.

(*To* COU.)—That pulse of pride you
    boast
    Within me beats as high;
    You and your titled host,
    Proud lord, I do defy!

FLO. (*Aside, with a glass in one hand and
    a leg of a bird in the other*).—
Upon my life, 'tis most unpleasant,
Just as one had attack'd a pheasant.

[THADDEUS, *who had taken up the purse,
and seeing himself and* DEVILSHOOF
*surrounded by the Nobles and Guests,
throws the purse at the* COUNT'S *feet.*

THA.—Take back your gold, and learn
    to know
    One — above aught you can
    bestow.

CHORUS OF NOBLES, &c.

Down with the daring slave
Who would our fury brave!

DEV.—Stand back, ye craven things!
    He who obstructs our path,
    Upon his rashness brings
    The vengeance of my wrath!

[DEVILSHOOF, *defending* THADDEUS,
*retreats, pressed upon by the Nobles,
Guests, &c., when the* COUNT *orders a
party of his Retainers to divide them;
they seize* DEVILSHOOF *and take him
into the castle.*

COU.—Seize him and bind him, and
    there let him find
    Escape from those walls better
    men have confined.

[*Here a party of Huntsmen and Retainers separate* THADDEUS *and* DEVILS-
HOOF; *they march* THADDEUS *off, and
exeunt among the rocks, while* DEVILS-
HOOF *is dragged into the castle.*

DEV. (*as they are dragging him off*).—
Tho' meshed by numbers in the yoke
    Of one by all abhorr'd,
    Yet tremble, worthless lord,
At the vengeance you thus provoke.

CHO.—Down with the slave
    Who would our fury brave!

[DEVILSHOOF *is dragged off into the
castle; the* COUNT, *Nobles, &c., reseat
themselves, when other dances are
introduced and the festival continues.*
BUDA *is seen to leave the window at
which she has been seated with* ARLINE,
and she enters and converses with the
COUNT. *In the midst of the most
joyous movements of the dance,* DEVILS-
HOOF *is seen descending from the roof
of the castle, until he reaches the window of* ARLINE'S *chamber, into which
he is seen to enter and to shut it
immediately.* BUDA *then enters the
castle, and in a minute afterwards the
festivities are interrupted by a violent
shrieking, the window is thrown open,
and* BUDA, *pale, and with dishevelled
hair, signifies by her gestures that*
ARLINE *has disappeared.*

CHO.—What sounds break on the air?
    What looks of wild despair
    A grief as wild impart?

COU.—My child! that word alone,
    With agonizing tone,
    Bursts in upon my heart!

[COUNT *and Nobles dash into the castle.
A general movement of all—some are
seen at the window of* ARLINE'S *chamber
signifying that she is gone.*

CHO.—Be every hand prepared
    Their liege lord's halls to guard,
    And with devotion's bond,
    All ties beyond.

FLO. (*kneeling, and appearing greatly
    alarmed*).—

Ah! what with dancing, screaming,
    fighting,
One really is a shocking plight in;
    It puzzles quite one's wit
    To find a place to pick a bit.

[*The* COUNT *rushes from the castle,
dragging* BUDA, *and followed by
Nobles.* BUDA, *trembling, falls on
her knees.*

XV

Cou.—Wretch! monster! give me back
    The treasure of my soul ;
    Go — all — the spoiler's foot-
      steps track
    That treasured prize who
      stole.

But no, vain hope ! unless we pray
  to Him
Who healeth all sorrow, with sup-
pliant limb.

PRAYER.

Thou who in might supreme
    O'er the fate of all reignest,
Thou who hope's palest beam
    In the mourner sustainest,
Vouchsafe to lend an ear
    To the grief of the wailer,
Cut short the dark career
    Of the ruthless assailer.

[*During the prayer,* DEVILSHOOF *is seen climbing up the rocks with* ARLINE *in his arms.*

CHORUS.

Follow, follow, with heart and with
  arm,
Follow, follow, and shelter from harm
    The pride of Arnheim's line,
    Where all its hopes entwine.

[*At the most animated part of the Chorus, bodies of Gentry, Retainers, Servants, &c., are seen rushing towards the rocks, and over every part, in pursuit of* DEVILSHOOF, *who, perceiving his situation, knocks away, the moment he has crossed it, the trunk of the tree which serves as a bridge between the two rocks, and thus bars their passage.* COUNT ARNHEIM, *in his distraction, is about to throw himself into the gulf —he is held back by attendants, into whose arms he falls senseless. Some are in the attitude of prayer—others menace* DEVILSHOOF, *who, folding* ARLINE *in his large cloak, disappears in the depths of the forest.*

ACT II.

NOTE.—Twelve years are supposed to elapse between the First and Second Acts.

SCENE I.

Street in Presburg, by moonlight. Tent of the Queen of the Gipsies, large curtains at the back—it is lighted by a lamp. On the opposite side of the stage are houses, one of which, a hotel, is lighted up.

[ARLINE *is discovered asleep on a tiger-skin—*THADDEUS *is watching over her. As the curtain rises, a Patrol of the City Guard marches by, and as soon as they are gone off* DEVILSHOOF *and a party of Gipsies, wrapped in cloaks, suddenly appear.*

CHORUS.

Silence, silence !—the lady moon
  Is the only witness now awake,
And weary of watching, 'chance she
    soon
  To sleep will herself betake.

Silence, silence !—from her throne in
    air,
She may look on, for aught we care ;
But if she attend unto our behest,
She will quietly go to her rest.

SOLO.
DEVILSHOOF.

There's a deed to do whose gains
Will reward the risk and the pains—

[*The Gipsies all draw their daggers and appear delighted.*

Fie, fie ! to a gentleman when you
  appeal,
You may draw his purse without
  drawing your steel ;
With bows, and politeness, and with
  great respect,
You may take more than he can at
  first suspect.

[*Pointing to the lighted windows of the hotel.*

See, where in goblets deep
What sense they have they steep.
Watch here ! till each to his home
  Shall reel on his doubtful way.
Watch here ! and the goblet's foam
  Will make each an easy prey.
Silence, silence ! this way, this way !

XVI

(CHORUS—Repeat.)

[As the Gipsies retire up the stage, FLORESTEIN *staggers out of the hotel—he is elegantly dressed, with chain, rings, &c., and a rich medallion round his neck.*

FLO.—Wine, wine! If I am heir
  To the Count—my uncle's—
   line— *[Hiccup.*
  Where's the fellow—will dare
  To refuse his nephew—wine?
       [Hiccup.
  That moon there, staring me
   on my way,
  Can't be as modest as people
   say,
  For meet whom she will, and
   in whatever spot,
  She often looks on at what she
   ought not.

[The Gipsies have by this time advanced, and DEVILSHOOF *goes politely up to* FLORESTEIN.

DEV.—My ear caught not the clock's
  last chime,
  And might I beg to ask the
   time?

*[*FLORESTEIN *reels, recovers a little, and after eyeing* DEVILSHOOF—

FLO. *(aside).*—If the bottle has pre-
  vailed,
   Yet whenever I'm as-
    sailed,
   Though there may be
    nothing in it,
   I am sobered in a min-
    ute—
(to DEV.) You are really so polite,
   That *(pulling out his
   watch)* 'tis late into
   the night.

*[*DEV. *takes the watch and puts it into his fob.*
  (assuming courage)—May I beg
  to ask——?

DEV.—I am grieved to see
  Anyone in such a state,
   And gladly will take the
    greatest care
   Of the rings and chains you
    chance to wear.

[Taking from FLORESTEIN *his rings, chain, and the rich medallion.* FLORESTEIN *draws his sword.*

FLO.—What I thought was politeness,
  is downright theft,
  And at this rate I soon shall
  have nothing left.

[At a sign from DEVILSHOOF *the Gipsies instantly surround* FLORESTEIN, *and take every valuable from him.*

CHO.—Advance with caution, let every
  man
   Seize on, and keep, whatever
   he can!

[During the Chorus, DEVILSHOOF *makes off with the medallion, and the others are dividing the rest of the spoil, when a female appears in the midst of them, drops her cloak, and discovers their* QUEEN. *The Gipsies appear stupefied.*

QUEEN—To him from whom you stole,
  Surrender back the WHOLE.

[The Gipsies return the different things to FLORESTEIN.

FLO. *(trembling and looking over the things).*—
  Thanks, Madam,—Lady—but
  might I request
  A medallion in diamonds—
  worth all the rest?

[At a sign from the QUEEN, *who seems to command its restitution.*

CHORUS OF GIPSIES.

On our chieftain's share we ne'er
 encroach,
And he fled with that prize at your
 approach.

QUE. *(to* FLORESTEIN).—Be your safety
    my care—

FLO. *(trembling).*—I'm in precious
  hands.

QUE. *(to Gipsies).*—Follow, and list
   to your Queen's
   commands.

CHO.—We follow, yes, and list unto
  our Queen's commands.

[*Exit* QUEEN, *holding* FLORESTEIN, *all of a tremble, with one hand, and beckoning the Gipsies to follow, with the other. As soon as they have gone off,* ARLINE, *who has been awakened by the noise, comes from the tent, followed by* THADDEUS.

ARL.—Where have I been wandering in my sleep? and what curious noise awoke me from its pleasant dream? Ah, Thaddeus, would you not like to know my dream? Well, I will tell it you.

THE GIPSY-GIRL'S DREAM.

I dreamt that I dwelt in marble halls,
  With vassals and serfs at my side,
And of all who assembled within those
    walls,
  That I was the hope and pride.
I had riches too great to count—
    could boast
  Of a high ancestral name;
And I also dreamt, which pleased me
    most,
      [*Taking both his hands in hers.*
  That you loved me still the same.

I dreamt that suitors sought my hand,
  That knights upon bended knee,
And with vows no maiden heart could
    withstand,
  They pledged their faith to me.
And I dreamt that one of that noble
    host
  Came forth my hand to claim;
But I also dreamt, which charmed me
    most,
  That you loved me still the same.

[*At the end of the ballad,* THADDEUS *presses* ARLINE *to his heart.*

ARL.—And do you love me still?

THA.—More than life itself.

ARL.—Yet is there a mystery between our affections and their happiness that I would fain unravel (*pointing to her arm*). The mark on this arm, which I have seen you so often contemplate, is the key to that mystery. By the love you say you bear me, solve it.

DUET.

THA. (*taking her hand and pointing to the mark*). —
That wound upon thine arm,
  Whose mark through life
    'twill be,
  In saving thee from greater
    harm,
  Was there transfixed by me.

ARL.—By thee?

THA.—Ere on thy gentle head
  Thy sixth sun had its radiance
    shed,
  A wild deer, who had lain at
    bay,
  Pursued by hunters cross'd
    thy way;

ARL.—Well?

THA.—By slaying him I rescued thee,

ARL.—Yes!

THA.—And in his death-throe's agony
  Thy tender form, by his antler
    gored,
  This humble arm to thy home
    restor'd.

ARL.—Strange feelings move this
    breast
  It never knew before,
  And bid me here implore
  That you reveal the rest.

THA.—The secret of her birth
  To me is only known,
  The secret of a life whose
    worth
  I prize beyond my own.

ARL.—The secret of my birth
  To him is only known,
  The secret of a life whose
    worth
  Perchance he will disown.

Ensemble.

ARL.—Speak, tell me, ease my tortured heart,
  And that secret, evil or good,
    impart.

THA.—I will tell thee all, tho' I lose thee for ever.

XVIII

ARL.—What is the spell hath yet effaced
The first fond lines that love hath traced,
And after-years have but imprest
More deep in love's confiding breast?

THA.—And yet few spells have e'er effaced
The first fond lines that love hath traced,
And after-years have but imprest
More deep in love's confiding breast.

Ensemble

[*At the end of the duet,* THADDEUS *throws himself, in an ecstasy, at the feet of* ARLINE, *and is bathing her hand with kisses, when the back curtains of the tent are withdrawn, and the* QUEEN *appears pale and trembling with passion. She advances towards* ARLINE, *and pointing to* THADDEUS—

QUE.—And dare you aspire to the love of him who possesses the heart of your Queen?

ARL.—I possess *his* heart, and will yield the possession to no one. He is the savior of my life, and the only friend that I have in all the tribe: he has sworn how much he loves me.

QUE.—Loves you!

ARL.—Yes; let him speak for himself, and choose between us.

QUE.—Be it so.

[THADDEUS, *who has been anxiously watching the two, here runs and embraces* ARLINE. *She surveys the* QUEEN *with an air of triumph.*

ARL. (*to the* QUEEN).—I made no idle boast. (*Then to* THADDEUS.) Summon our comrades hither.

[*The* QUEEN *is standing in the centre, while* THADDEUS *calls the Gipsies together, who enter on all sides and surround the* QUEEN, *and appear to ask what is going on.*

CONCERTED PIECE.

ARL.—Listen, while I relate
The hopes of the Gipsy's fate.
I am loved by one, by one I love
All other hearts above,
And the sole delight to me
[*Taking the hand of* THADDEUS.
Is with him united to be.

CHO.—Happy and light of heart are those
Who in each bosom one faith repose!

DEV. (*Aside—maliciously pointing at the* QUEEN).—
A rival's hate you may better tell
By her rage than by her tears,
And it, perchance, may be as well
To set them both by the ears.

(*To* QUE.)—As Queen of our tribe, 'tis yours by right,
The hands of those you rule to unite.

CHO. (*to the* QUEEN, *who draws back and hesitates*).
In love and truth, by thee
Their hands united be.

QUE. (*haughtily advancing and taking the hands of* ARLINE *and* THADDEUS).—
Hand to hand, and heart to heart,
Who shall those I have mated part?
By the spell of my sway,
Part them who may.
[*Joining their hands.*

CHO.—Happy and light of heart are those
Who in each bosom one faith repose.

[CHORUS *lie down, assuming picturesque attitudes.* QUEEN *comes forward; segue ballad.*

XIX

BALLAD.

QUE.—Oh, would that I had died ere
  now,
  For then I had not felt
The bitter pang, the crushing
  blow,
  Thy cruel words have dealt!
I've but one solace—Heaven
  grant
  It cheer me to the last!
'Tis sad, fond mem'ry, faithful
  still
  To bliss for ever past.

But no! but no! not one poor
  ray
  Of comfort will be mine,
No gleam of hope, however
  faint,
  Will thro' my sorrow shine!
That sorrow is so sharp, so
  great,
  Its pow'r so deep, so vast,
That e'en the mem'ry will it
  crush
  Of bliss for ever past.

[*During this scene the stage has been
growing somewhat lighter.*

A Gipsy enters.

GIP.—Morning is beginning to
dawn, and crowds of people are already flocking towards the fair; the
sports begin with daylight.

QUE.—Summon the rest of the tribe,
and meet me forthwith in the public
square. (*To* DEVILSHOOF.) Do you
remain to bear my further orders.

[*Exeunt* THADDEUS *and* ARLINE *hand
in hand, followed by the other Gipsies
repeating Chorus.*

CHO.—In the Gipsy's life you read,
  &c.

DUET.

QUE.—This is thy deed!—seek not
  t'assuage
  My jealous fears, a rival's rage.

DEV.—I neither fear, nor seek to calm.

QUE. (*aside to* DEVILSHOOF).—
  Revenge is the wounded bosom's balm.

That jewel with which thou
  hast dared to deck
  Thy foredoomed neck,
Answer me—where did'st thou
  get it—where?

DEV.—'Twas entrusted to my care.

QUE.—This very night, on this very
  spot,
  Thy soul for once its fears forgot,
And a drunken galliard, who
  cross'd thy way,
  Became thy prey—

DEV. (*aside*).—Fiend-born! 'twere vain
  to fly
  The glance of her searching
  eye.

QUE.—Down on thy knees, the
  gem restore,
  E'en in thy shame amazed,
Or long years of sin shall
  deplore
  The storm which thou
  has raised.

DEV.(*aside*).—It best might be the
  prize to restore,
  Much as I seem amazed;
Or hereafter I may de-
  plore
  The storm which I have
  raised.

Ensemble

[*Kneeling and presenting the medallion to
to the* QUEEN.
  Queen, I obey.

QUE.—   'Tis the wisest thing
  Thy miscreant heart could do.
[*Takes medallion.*

DEV. (*aside*)—Who from my grasp
  such prize could wring,
  The doing it may rue.

QUE.—Depart, and join the rest.

DEV.—I do thy high behest.
 (*aside*). The wrongs we forgive
  not and cannot forget,
  Will our vengeance more
  sharply whet

QUE.—The wrongs we forgive not
  and cannot forget,
  Will our vengeance more
  sharply whet.

Ensemble

[*Exeunt the* QUEEN *and* DEVILSHOOF *at
opposite sides.*

XX

Scene II.

Another Street in Presburg.   Daylight.

[Enter Arline, *in a fanciful dress, followed by a troup of Gipsies.   She has a tambourine in her hand.*

CHORUS.

In the Gipsy's life you read
The life that all would like to lead

SONG.
Arline.

Come with the Gipsy bride!
  And repair to the fair,
  Where the mazy dance
  Will the hours entrance,
Where souls as light preside!

Life can give nothing beyond
One heart you know to be fond,
Wealth, with its hoards, cannot buy
The peace content can supply,
And rank in its halls cannot find
The calm of a happy mind.

Love is the first thing to clasp,
But if he escape your grasp,
Friendship will then be at hand,
In the young rogue's place to stand;
Hope will then be nothing loth
To point out the way to both.

CHORUS.

In the Gipsy's life you read
The life that all would like to lead.

[Exit Arline, *followed by the tribe of Gipsies.*

Scene III.

A Grand Fair in the Public Platz of Presburg.   On one side a large hotel, over which is inscribed "The Hall of Justice."   Various groups of Gentry, Soldiers, Citizens, and Peasantry cover the stage.   Foreign shops are seen in various parts, curious Rope Dancers, Showmen, Waxwork, a Quack Doctor, Exhibitions, &c., &c., are dispersed here and there.   Flags hung out at the windows and ringing of bells enliven the scene.

CHORUS.

Life itself is at the best
One scene in mask of folly drest,
And there is no part of its wild career,
But you will meet with here!
To these symbols of life your voices
  swell,
Vive la masque, et vive la bagatelle!

[At the end of the Chorus and during the Symphony, a movement is perceived at the further end of the place, which is followed by the entrance of a double party of men Gipsies headed by Devilshoof *and* Thaddeus, *who force a passage down the centre of the stage, which they occupy; they then open their ranks, when another file of female Gipsies, headed by their* Queen *and* Arline, *passes down them;* Florestein *and a party are seen watching them with great curiosity.*

QUARTET.
Arline, Queen, Thaddeus, and Devilshoof.

From the valleys and hills
  Where the sweetest buds grow,
And are watered by rills
  Which are purest that flow—
Come we! come we!

CHORUS.

Light of heart, fleet of foot, reckless
  of slight or gibe,
Who can compare with the free, happy
  Gipsy tribe!

[During this, some of the Gipsies have been enacting characteristic dances, when Arline, *carrying a flower basket in her hand, glides round to the assembled company and sits down.*

SOLO.
Arline.

Sir Knight and lady, listen!

(To a lady.)—
That bright eye seems to glisten
As if his trusted tale
Did o'er thy sense prevail!

(To another—pointing to her heart).—
Pretty maiden, pray take care,
Love is making havoc there!

(To a third—pointing to a ring on her finger).—
This token which from love you
  borrow,
The prelude is of many a sorrow:
There are those have lived to know
The Gipsy's words are true.

Cho. *(as the dance of the Gipsies continues).*—
Life itself is at the best
One scene in mask of folly drest,
And there is no part of its wild career,
But you will meet with here!

[*At the end of the dance and Chorus,* COUNT ARNHEIM *and some Officers of State enter ; his hair has become gray, his step is slow, and his appearance is that of sorrow. He is accosted by* FLORESTEIN.

FLO.—My dear uncle, it delights me to see you amongst us, and here is a little Gipsy girl that would delight you still more (*aside*) if you had my blood in your veins ; she's positively a charming creature.

COU.—I have lost the taste of joy, and the sight of youth and beauty recalls to my memory that treasure of both, my loved and lost Arline.

[*He gazes attentively at* ARLINE, *sighs heavily, then exit with his retinue into the Hall of Justice.*

FLO. (*to a party of his friends*).—It's no use restraining me—I'm positively smitten. (*Breaks from them and goes up to* ARLINE.) Fair creature, your manner has enchanted me, and I would fain take a lesson from you.

ARL.—In politeness, sir ? By all means. To begin, then, whenever you address a lady, take your hat off.

FLO.—Very smart (*with a titter*)— 'pon my word — very smart. Your naïveté only increases the feeling of admiration and devotion which a too suspectible heart—

ARL. (*bursting out laughing*).— Ha ! ha ! ha !

FLO.—Your indifference will drive me to despair.

ARL.—Will it really ?

FLO.—Do not mock me, but pity my too susceptible nature, and let me print one kiss upon—

[*Here* ARLINE *gives him a violent slap on the face; the* QUEEN, *who has gone up the stage with* THADDEUS, *now brings him on one side and points out the situation of* ARLINE *and* FLORE-STEIN; *he is about to rush upon* FLORE-STEIN *just as* ARLINE *has slapped the latter's face, who on turning round finds himself between the two, both laughing in his face.*

QUE. (*eyeing* FLORESTEIN).—It is the very person from whom they stole the trinkets I made them give him back again.

[*Taking the medallion from her bosom.*

This, too, is his, and now my project thrives.

[FLORESTEIN *turns up the stage to join his party, and the* QUEEN *crosses to* ARLINE.

You have acted well your part, and thus your Queen rewards you. (*Places the medallion round her neck.*) Forget not the hand that gave it.

ARL. (*kneeling and kissing the* QUEEN'S *hand*).—Let this bespeak my gratitude.

QUE.—And now let our tribe depart.

[*Chorus and dance repeated, and the Gipsies are all about to march off.* THADDEUS *and* ARLINE *bring up the rear of their body, and, as they are going off,* FLORESTEIN, *who, with his friends, has been watching their departure, perceives his medallion on the neck of* ARLINE ; *he breaks through the crowd and stops her ; she and* THAD-DEUS *come forward.*

FLO.—Though you treated me so lightly some moments past, you will not do so now. That medallion is mine ; my friends here recognize it.

ALL—We do ! we do !

[*Here* DEVILSHOOF *is seen to steal off.*

FLO.—And I accuse you of having stolen it.

ARL.—Stolen ! It was this instant given me by our Queen, and she is here to verify my words.

[ARLINE *runs about, looking everywhere for the* QUEEN. ·

FLO.—That's an everyday sort of subterfuge. (*To the crowd.*) Worthy people and friends, that medallion on her neck belongs to me, and I accuse her or her accomplices of having robbed me.

XXII

CONCERTED PIECE.

Chorus of Populace surrounding ARLINE.

Shame! shame! let us know
  the right,
And shame on the guilty one
  alight!

THA. (*rushing before* ARLINE *to shield
  her*).—

He who a hand on her would
  lay,
Through my heart must force
  his way!

CHO.—Tear them asunder, but still
  protect
Until they can prove what they
  suspect.

ARL—To all who their belief have lent,
  Heaven can attest, I'm innocent.

[FLORESTEIN, *who has during this movement entered the Hall of Justice, is
now seen returning, followed by a strong
guard, who file off each side of the steps.*

FLO. (*to Captain of Guard, pointing to*
  ARLINE).—

There stands the culprit, on
  you I call;
Conduct her away to the Hall!

CHO.—To the Hall!

[ARLINE *looks at him with great contempt;
the Gipsies, perceiving her danger,
range themselves around her.* THAD-
DEUS *breaks from those who are
holding him, and rushes up to her.*
FLORESTEIN *has got behind the* CAP-
TAIN OF THE GUARD, *who gives orders
for his men to seize* ARLINE, *upon
which the Gipsies draw their daggers.
A conflict ensues, in which the Guard
maintains possession of* ARLINE. *A
body of the populace reseize* THADDEUS,
and the Gipsies are routed.

CAP. OF G.—They who would
  brave the law,
  Against themselves but
  draw!

FLO., GUARDS.—To the Hall!
  away to the Hall!

THA.—Free me, or else the law
  Upon your heads you draw!

GIP.—Why should we fear the law,
  Or all the arms you draw?

ARL.—I'm innocent!

Ensemble.

[ARLINE *is conducted by a file of the
Guard, led by the* CAPTAIN, *and preceded by* FLORESTEIN *and his party into
the Hall of Justice; the people follow
in a mass, while* THADDEUS *is detained
by those who first seized him, and as*
ARLINE *is going up the steps, the
figure of the* QUEEN *is seen in an attitude of triumph over her rival's fall.*

SCENE IV.

Interior of COUNT ARNHEIM'S *apartment in the Hall of Justice—a view of
the last scene visible through one of the
windows at the back. A full-length portrait of* ARLINE, *as she was in the first
Act, hangs on the wall; state chairs, &c.
An elevation or dais on the* (O.P.) *side.*

[COUNT ARNHEIM *enters, thoughtful and
dejected; he contemplates* ARLINE'S
*portrait, and wipes a tear from his
eye.*

RECITATIVE.

Whate'er the scenes the present hour
  calls forth before the sight,
They lose their splendor when com-
  pared with scenes of past delight.

SONG.

The heart bow'd down by weight of
  woe
  To weakest hope will cling,
To thought and impulse while they
  flow,
  That can no comfort bring.
With those exciting scenes will blend,
  O'er pleasure's pathway thrown,
But mem'ry is the only friend
  That grief can call its own.

The mind will, in its worst despair
  Still ponder o'er the past,
On moments of delight that were
  Too beautiful to last.
To long-departed years extend
  Its visions with them flown;
For mem'ry is the only friend
  That grief can call its own.

[*At the end of the song, a confused noise
is heard outside, when the* CAPTAIN OF
THE GUARD *enters.*

CAP.—A robbery has been committed, and the accused is now in the
Hall awaiting the pleasure of your
lordship, as chief magistrate of the
city, for examination.

XXIII

Cou.—Bring the parties before me.

[*The* CAPTAIN *arranges the magisterial chair* (O.P.), *bows, and exit.*

Anything to arouse me from these distracting thoughts, though the sole happiness I now enjoy is in the recollection of my long-lost child.

[*Seats himself, when the doors are violently opened, and a mob of Citizens, Guards and Gentry enter.* FLORESTEIN, *who is in the midst of them, instantly rushes up to the* COUNT.

FLO.—It is your lordship's nephew—I, who have been robbed!

COU.—Some folly of yours is for ever compromising my name and that of your family.

FLO.—But I am in this instance the victim—I have been robbed, and there stands the culprit.

[*Pointing to* ARLINE *standing in the centre, pale and with dishevelled hair, but still haughty in her demeanor.*

COU. (*aside*).—'Tis she I saw but now in the public square. That girl—so young, so beautiful—commit a robbery? Impossible!

FLO.—She stole this medallion belonging to me—we found it upon her.

COU. (*addressing* ARLINE).—Can this be true?

ARL. (*looking contemptuously at* FLORESTEIN, *and turning with dignity to the* COUNT).—Heaven knows I am innocent, and if your lordship knew my heart, *you* would not deem me guilty.

COU. (*aside*).—Her words sink deep into my breast. Childless myself, I fain would spare the child of another. (*To* FLORESTEIN).—What proofs have you of this?

FLO. (*pointing to his friends*).—My witnesses are here, who all can swear they saw it on her neck.

ALL.—We can.

COU.—Still does my mind misgive me. (*To* ARLINE, *in a kind tone.*) My wish is to establish your innocence—explain this matter to me and without fear.

ARL.—That medallion was given to me by the Queen of the tribe to which I belong—how it came in her possession, I know not. But a light breaks in upon me—I see it all—I chanced to incur her displeasure, and to revenge herself upon me she has laid for me this shameful snare, into which I have innocently fallen, and of which I have become the victim.

[*Hiding her face in her hands and weeping.*

COU. (*with a struggle*).—I believe your tale, and from my heart I pity the inexperience which has led to the ruin of one who seems above the grade of those she herds with; but in the fulfilment of duty I must compromise the feelings of nature, and I am forced to deliver you into the hands of justice.

ARL. (*to the* COUNT).—To you, my earthly, to Him, my heavenly, Judge I reassert my innocence. I may be accused, but will not be degraded, and from the infamy with which I am unjustly threatened, thus I free myself.

[*She draws a dagger from beneath her scarf, and is about to stab herself, when* COUNT ARNHEIM *rushes forward, seizes her arm and wrests the dagger from her.*

FINALE.

COU.—Hold! hold!
    We cannot give the life we
        take,
    Nor re-unite the heart we
        break!

[*Taking the hand of* ARLINE, *and suddenly seeing the wound on her arm.*

What visions round me rise,
And cloud with the mists of the
    past mine eyes?
That mark! Those features! and
    thy youth!

[*Dragging* ARLINE *forward, and in great agitation.*

My very life hangs on thy truth—
How came that mark?

XXIV

ARL. (*recollecting* THADDEU.'s *words*).—
Ere on my head
My sixth sun had its radiance shed,
A wild deer, who had lain at bay,
Pursued by hunters, cross'd my way;
My tender form, by his antler gor'd,
An humble youth to my home restor'd.
The tale he but this day confess'd,
And is near at hand to relate the rest.

[*Here a tumult is heard, and* THADDEUS,
*having escaped from those who confined
him, breaks into the room, and rushes
into the arms of* ARLINE. *The
* COUNT, *on seeing him, reels back. A
general excitement prevails.*

COU.—With the force of fear and hope
My feelings have to cope.

ARL. (*Approaching the* COUNT, *and
pointing to* THADDEUS, *who
starts on beholding him*).—
'Tis he the danger braved—
'Tis he my life who saved!

SOLO.

COU. (*Seizing* ARLINE *in his arms in a
transport of joy*).—
Mine own, my long-lost child!
Oh, seek not to control
This frantic joy, this wild
Delirium of my soul!
Bound in a father's arms,
And pillowed on his breast,
Bid all those wild alarms
That assail'd thy feelings, rest.

[COUNT *clasps* ARLINE *to his heart;
kisses her head, hands, and hair,
shedding tears of joy.*

ARL. (*Bewildered, starts from the*
COUNT, *and runs to* THAD-
DEUS).—
Speak—speak! this shaken
frame,
This doubt, this torture, see!
My hopes—my very life—my
fame
Depend on thee!

THA. (*Pointing to* COUNT ARNHEIM,
with deep emotion, aside).—
Dear as thou long hast been,
Dear as thou long wilt be,
Mourned as this passing scene
Will be through life by me,
Though this heart, and none other
like mine can adore thee,
Yet (*aloud*) thou art not deceived—
'TIS thy father before thee!

[ARLINE *staggers, and then rushes into
the* COUNT'S *arms*

CHO.—Praised be the will of
Heav'n,
Whose pure light upon
them smiled,
And whose bounty thus
hath given
The father fond his
child!

COU.—Prais'd be the will of
Heav'n,
Whose pure light upon
me smiled,
And whose bounty thus
hath given
To a father fond his
child!

ARL., FLO.—Prais'd be the will of
Heav'n,
Whose light o'er ($^{me}_{them}$)
smiled,
And whose bounty hath
given
A father his child!

THA.—Though from this bosom
riven,
That heart is beguil'd,
The bereavement hath
giv'n
The father his child!

[THADDEUS *hides his face in his
hands, much moved.*

DEV. (*Suddenly emerging from the
crowd, and dragging* THAD-
DEUS *away*).—
Better to go now ere
driven
Than for ever be revil'd,
For Heav'n's bounty thus
hath giv'n
To a father fond his
child!

CHO.—Praised be the will of
Heav'n,
Whose pure light upon
them smiled,
And whose bounty thus
hath giv'n
To a father fond his
child!

Ensemble

XXV

ACT III.

SCENE I.

A splendid saloon in the castle of COUNT ARNHEIM. *On the ground floor a large window at the back opening on the Park. On the* (O.P.) *side the door of a small cabinet; doors at the back leading into spacious galleries.*

Enter ARLINE, *elegantly dressed for a ball.*

ARL.—The past appears to me but a dream, from which I have at length awakened. Yet my heart recalls enough to convince me it was all reality. When I think of the wandering life I led, my memory will revert to him who in every trial preserved its honor, who twice restored me to a father's arms, and at length to a father's home.

COUNT ARNHEIM *enters with* FLORESTEIN—ARLINE *runs into his arms.*

COU.—Every moment you leave me is a moment of unhappiness. I am jealous of whatever divides us, short as may be the interval. On a night of so much joy, when so many friends are to assemble and participate in your father's delight, let me intercede for one you have too much cause to be angry with.

ARL. (*averting her head*).—The very sight of him disturbs me. (*To the* COUNT.) The wishes of my dear father I would cheerfully comply with, but this repugnance I cannot overcome.

FLO. (*falling on his knee*).—Fair cousin, let me plead my own cause, and express the—aw— sorrow I really feel at having for an instant believed it possible—in fact, I never in reality—

Enter a SERVANT.

What the devil do you want at such a critical part of one's conversation?

[SERVANT *crosses to the* COUNT.

SER.—The castle is filling with guests who inquire for your lordship. [*Exit.*

COU. (*to* ARLINE).—Let us hasten to meet them, and afford me the joy of making you known to all.

ARL.—Allow me but time to fortify myself for a ceremony I am a stranger to, and I will follow you.

FLO.—That is but reasonable, uncle —I will live in hopes of my cousin's forgiveness, which can alone restore my—peace—of mind. [*Aside.*] I shall positively expire if I don't lead off the first quadrille with her.

[*Exeunt* COUNT *and* FLORESTEIN.

ARL.—I am once more left to my thoughts and all the deep regrets which accompany them ; nothing can drive the recollection of Thaddeus from my mind, and the lonely life I led was to me far happier than the constrained one I now pass ; and the graceful dress of the Gipsy-girl becomes me more than all this gaudy apparel of nobility. (*Going round the room to see if any one is watching.*) Now no eye beholds me, I may at least indulge in a remembrance of the past. (*Goes to the cabinet* (O.P.) *and brings out her Gipsy dress.*) The sight of this recalls the memory of happy days, and of him who made them happy.

[*As she is contemplating the dress, the window at the back suddenly opens, and* DEVILSHOOF *springs into the apartment.*

ARL. (*screaming*).—Ah ! what seek you here with me ?

DEV.—Hush ! fear not ; but be silent. I come to ask you to rejoin our tribe— we have never ceased to feel the loss of one liked more than all the rest.

ARL.—Impossible ! Leave me, I pray, and let me forget we have ever been acquainted.

DEV.—I have brought with me one who has, undoubtedly, greater powers of persuasion than I can pretend to.

XXVI

[*Here* THADDEUS *appears at the window, enters the room, and* ARLINE, *unable to restrain her feelings, rushes into his arms.*

THA.—In the midst of so much luxury, so much wealth and grandeur, I thought you had forgotten me.

ARL.—Forgotten you! Had I nothing else to remind me of you, this (*pointing to the Gipsy dress*) would always speak to me of you. Forgotten you!

THA.—The scenes in which you now move may drive from your memory every trace of the past, and I only come to ask—to hope—that you will sometimes think upon me.

[DEVILSHOOF *goes up to the window, on the lookout.*

AIR.

When other lips and other hearts
   Their tales of love shall tell,
In language whose excess imparts
   The power they feel so well:
There may, perhaps, in such a scene,
   Some recollection be
Of days that have as happy been,
   And you'll remember me!

When coldness or deceit shall slight
   The beauty now they prize,
And deem it but a faded light
   Which beams within your eyes;
When hollow hearts shall wear a mask
   'Twill break your own to see,
In such a moment I but ask
   That you'll remember me!

[*At the end of the song,* ARLINE *goes up to* THADDEUS, *and with great emphasis says—*

ARL.—Whatever may be our future lot, nothing should persuade you that I can ever cease to think of—ever cease to love you.

THA. (*overjoyed*).—My heart is overpowered with happiness. Yet, alas! 'tis but of short duration, for I must leave you now for ever.

ARL.—Oh, no, no! say not so! I cannot live without you.

THA.—And will you then forsake your home, your kindred, all, and follow me?

TRIO.

THA. (*to* ARLINE).—
Through the world wilt thou fly, love,
   From the world with me?
Wilt thou Fortune's frowns defy, love?
   As I will for thee?

ARL. (*to* THADDEUS).—
Through the world I would fly, love,
   From the world with thee,
Could I hush a father's sigh, love,
   That would heave for me.

DEV. (*coming down — to* THADDEUS).—
All the world hither fly,
   Come away with me!
Never let a lover's sigh
   Ruin bring on thee!

Ensemble.

DEV. (*still looking out*).—
   A moment more, and your doom is cast!

ARL. (*aside*).—The hopes that were brightest, the dreams of the past, In the fullness of promise recede, And render the prospect dark indeed.

DEV.—Escape is hopeless.

ARL. (*pointing to the cabinet*).—Enter here, Where detection we need not fear!

[THADDEUS *has barely time to take refuge in the cabinet, and* DEVILSHOOF *to escape by the window, when the great doors are thrown open, and a brilliant assemblage enters, led by* COUNT ARNHEIM, FLORESTEIN, *&c.* COUNT *takes* ARLINE'S *hand and presents her to the company.*

COU. — Welcome, welcome all — share with me all the joy I feel, while I present my loved and long-lost daughter.

XXVII

FINALE.

CHO.—Welcome the present, oh, pon-
  der not
   On the days departed now,
  Let the cares that were theirs
   be forgot,
    And 'ras'd from pleasure's
    brow;
  Never mind Time, nor what he
   has done,
  If he the present will smile
   upon.

FLO. (*seeing the Gipsy dress on a chair
  and taking it up*).—
   This garment is not fit to
   grace,
   At such a moment, such a
   place,
   And 'twere best to hide the
   prize
   In this recess (*pointing to cabinet*) from his lordship's
   eyes.

ARL. (*whose attention has been riveted on
  the cabinet, and seeing FLORE-
  STEIN go near it*).—
   That room and its treasure
   belong to me,
   And from all intrusion must
   sacred be.

CHO.—Welcome the present, oh, pon-
  der not
   On the days departed now.

[*A confused murmur is heard at the back
of the stage.*

   What sound breaks in upon
   the ear,
   Checking young joy's career?

[*A Female, closely veiled, enters the apartment, and goes up to* COUNT ARNHEIM.

FEM.—Heed the warning voice!
   Wail, and not rejoice!
   The foe to thy rest
   Is one thou lov'st best.

[*She lets her veil fall, and discovers the*
QUEEN OF THE GIPSIES.

COU.—Who and what art thou? Let
  me know
   Whom thou dost deem my foe?

QUE.—Think not my warning wild,
   'Tis thy refound child.
  She loves a youth of the tribe
   I sway,
   And braves the world's re-
   proof;
  List to the words I say—
   He is now conceal'd beneath
   thy roof!

COU.—Base wretch, thou liest!

QUE.—Thy faith I begrudge—
   Open that door, and thyself be
   judge!

[COUNT *rushes to the door of the cabinet;*
ARLINE *in vain opposes.*

COU.—Stand not across my path! ⎞
   Brave not a father's wrath! ⎟
              ⎬ *Ensemble.*
ARL.—Thrown thus across thy ⎟
   path,   ⎟
   Let me abide thy wrath! ⎠

[*The* COUNT *pushes* ARLINE *aside, opens
the door, and* THADDEUS *appears; the*
COUNT *reels back, and every one seems
panic-stricken.*

QUINTET AND CHORUS.

COUNT, FLORESTEIN, THADDEUS, AR-
LINE, and QUEEN.

COU. (*to* ARLINE.)—   ⎞
   To shame and feeling dead, ⎟
   Now hopeless to deplore, ⎟
   The thunder bursting o'er ⎟
   my head,   ⎟
   Had not surprised me ⎟
   more.   ⎟
              ⎟
FLO.—And this is why she said, ⎟
   I must not touch the ⎬ *Ensemble.*
   door;   ⎟
   It clearly would have been ⎟
   ill-bred,   ⎟
   For rivals are a bore!   ⎟
              ⎟
THA.—Though every hope be fled, ⎟
   Which seemed so bright ⎟
   before,   ⎟
   The vengeance I would ⎟
   scorn to dread,   ⎟
   Which they on me can ⎠
   pour!

16118

ARL. (*horror-stricken on seeing the* QUEEN) —
    To all but vengeance dead,
        She stands mine eyes
            before !
    Its thunders waiting on my
            head
        In all her hate)
        She only lives) to pour.

QUE. (*maliciously eyeing* ARLINE).—
    All other feelings dead,
        Revenge can hope re-
            store,
    Its thunders on her daring
            head
        I only live to pour.

CHO.—Although to feeling dead,
        This sorrow we deplore,
    The thunder bursting o'er
            our head,
        Had not surprised us
            more.

Ensemble.

COU. (*advancing to* THADDEUS).—
    Leave the place thy polluting
        step hath cross'd !
    Depart, or thou art lost !

THA. (*casting a sorrowful look on* AR-
    LINE *as he is about to go*).—
    To threats I should contemn,
    For thy dear sake I yield.

ARL. (*summoning resolution*).—
    The bursting torrent I will
        stem,
    And him I live for, shield.

[*She takes* THADDEUS *by the hand, and
goes to the* COUNT, *then turns to the
company.*

    Break not the only tie
        That bids my heart rejoice,
    For whom contented I would die—
    (*With energy.*) The husband of my
            choice.

COU. (*rushing between them and drawing
    his sword. To* THADDEUS).—

    Depart, ere my thirsty weapon
        stains
    These halls with the blood of thy
        recreant veins !

(*To* ARLINE) —
    False thing ! beloved too long,
        too well,
    Brave not the madness thou canst
        not quell !

QUE. (*seizing* THADDEUS *by the arm*).—
    List to the warning voice that
        calls thee !
    Fly from the peril which enthralls
        thee !

[*Darting a furious look at* ARLINE *as
she passes her.*

    Weep rivers—for ages pine !
    He shall never be thine !

[*As the* QUEEN *is dragging* THADDEUS
towards the window, ARLINE *stops him.*

ARL. (*to the assembly*).—
    Your pardon if I seek
    With my father alone to speak.

[*Exeunt omnes at the large doors* (*beside
the windows*), *which close upon them;
the* QUEEN *is seen to pass out of the
window.*

ARL. (*falling at the* COUNT'S *feet*).—
    See at your feet a suppliant—one
    Whose place should be your heart;
    Behold the only living thing
    To which she had to cling ;
    Who saved her life, watched o'er
        her years
    With all the fondness faith en-
        dears,
    And her affections won—
    Rend not such ties apart !

COU.—Child ! Arline ! wilt thou ?
        darest thou heap
    A stain thine after-life will e'er
        weep,
    On these hairs, by thee and sor-
        row bleach'd—
    On this heart, dishonor never
        reached ?

ARL. (*rising and seeking refuge in the
    arms of* THADDEUS).—
    Whatever the danger, the ruin,
        the strife—
    It must fall; united we are for life.

COU. (*with rage*) —
    United ! and wouldst thou link
        my name
    In a chain of such disgrace ?
    My rank, my very blood defame
    With a blot no time can efface?
    The child of my heart, of my
        house the pride,
    An outcast Gipsy's bride !

XXIX

Tha. (*breaking from her, and going up with great dignity to* Count Arnheim).—

> Proud lord, although this head
>   proscribed
> Should fall by the weapons thy
>   wealth hath bribed,
> Although in revealing the name
>   I bear,
> The home I shall see no more—
> The land which to thee, in its
>   deep despair,
> The deadliest hatred bore—
> I may fall, as have fallen the
>   bravest of foes,
> 'Twere better like them to die,
> And in honored earth to lie,
> Than hear, unresented, reproaches
>   like those.

[Count Arnheim *and* Arline *betray symptoms of astonishment, yet great anxiety.*

> Start not, but listen !

> When the fair land of Poland was
>   ploughed by the hoof
> Of the ruthless invader, when
>   Might,
> With steel to the bosom and flame to
>   the roof,
> Completed her triumph o'er Right,
> In that moment of danger, when
>   Freedom invoked
> All the fetterless sons of her pride,
> In a phalanx as dauntless as Freedom
>   e'er yok'd,
> I fought and I bled by her side.
> My birth is noble, unstained my crest
> As is thine own—let this attest !

[*Takes his commission, seen in Act I, from his bosom, and gives it to the* Count, *who stands fixed and bewildered.*

> Pity for one in childhood torn
> From kindred with whom she dwelt,
> Ripened in after-years to love—
> The fondest that heart hath felt—
> Has made me, thus far, faith renew
> With outlaws chance first link'd me to.
> As a foe, on this head let your hatred
>   be pil'd,
> But despise not one who hath so loved
>   your child.

Cou. (*greatly moved*).—

> The feuds of a nation's strife,
> The party storms of life,
> Should never their sorrows impart
> To the calmer scenes of the heart.
> By this hand let thine hold
> Till the blood in its veins be cold !

[Thaddeus, *moved to tears, is about to fall at the feet of the* Count, *who checks him.*

> Not at mine—be that homage
>   paid at hers,
> Who the firmest affection on thee
>   confers.

TRIO.

Count, Arline, Thaddeus.

> Let not the soul o'er sorrows grieve,
> With which the bosom hath ceased
>   to heave ;
> Let us not think of the tempest past,
> If we reach the haven at last.

[*During the trio, the wan figure of the* Queen *has been seen at the window in the back; and at the end of it, as* Thaddeus *is about to embrace* Arline, *the* Queen, *in a transport of rage, points him out to a Gipsy by her side, who is in the act of firing at him, when* Devilshoof, *who has tracked their steps, averts the Gipsy's aim, and by a rapid movement turns the musket towards the* Queen—*it goes off, and she falls.*

Cou.—Guard every portal—summon
>   each guest and friend—
> And this festive scene suspend.

[*The distant sound of joyous instruments heard in the saloons, which the intelligence of the catastrophe is supposed to have reached, ceases, and crowds of Nobles, Ladies, Guests, &c., pour in at each door.* Arline *rushes into the arms of* Thaddeus, *and then passes over to the* Count.

Arline *and* Chorus.

> Oh ! what full delight
>   Through my bosom thrills,
> And a wilder glow
>   In my heart instils !

> Bliss unfelt before,
>   Hope without alloy,
> Speak, with raptured tone,
>   Of my heart the joy !

[*As the curtain descends, there is heard, under the window at the back,*

THE GIPSIES' CHORUS.

> In the Gipsy's life you read
> The life that all would like to lead.

Index.

XXXI

16118

The Bohemian Girl.
Overture.

M. W. BALEE.

Moderato.

Piano.

Larghetto.

Allegro.

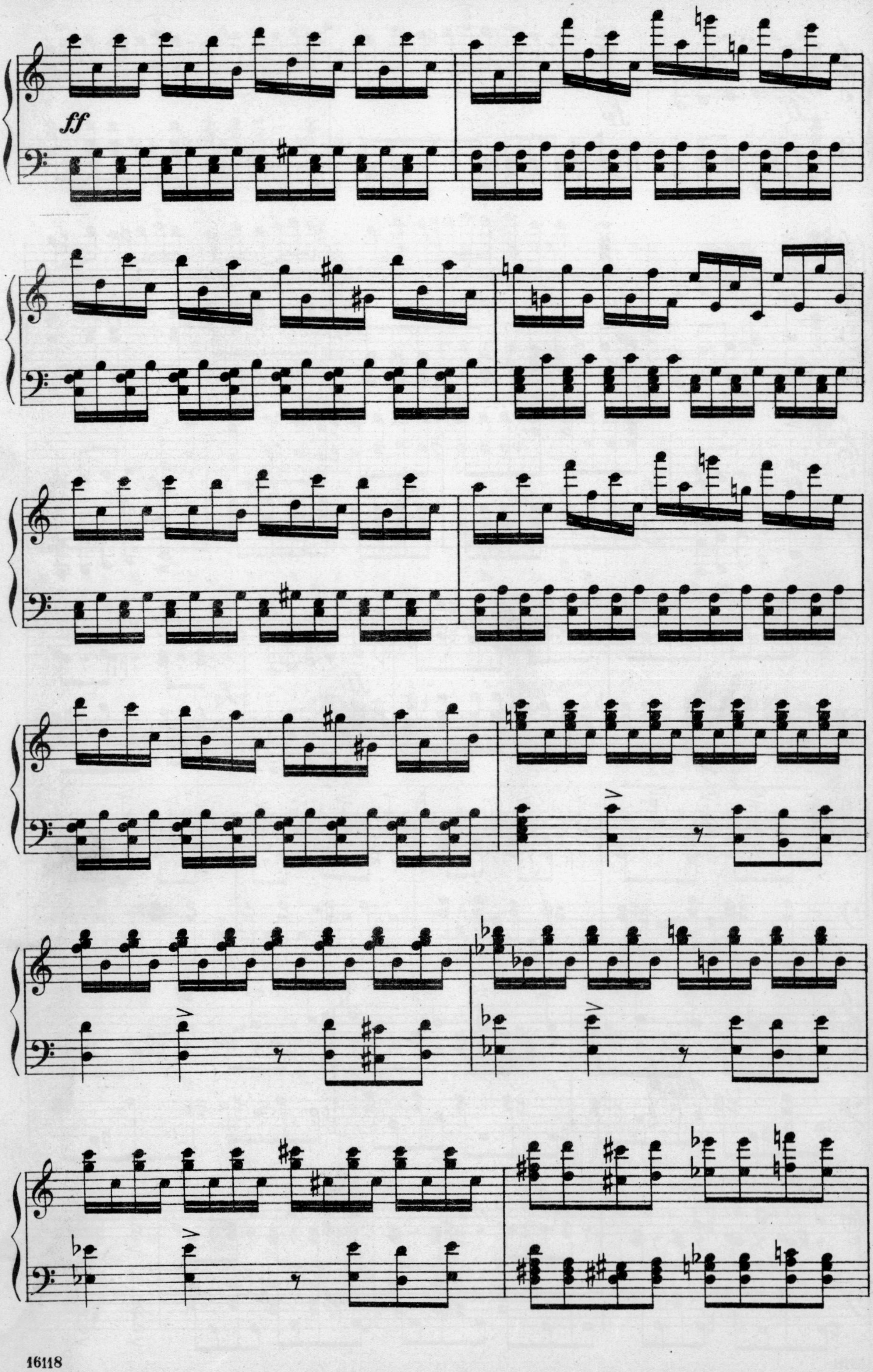
ff

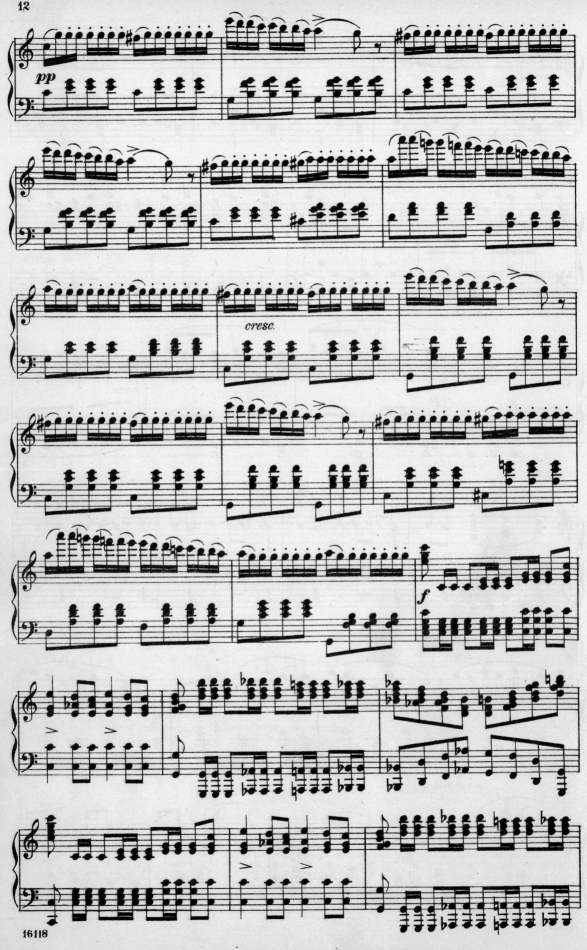

Più mosso.

Scene I. — The château and grounds of Count Arnhëim, on the Danube, near Presburg. On one side, principal entrance of the castle; opposite is a statue of the Emperor, above which a party is employed raising the Austrian flag. On the rising of the curtain, the retainers of Count Arnheim are discovered preparing for the chase.

Introduction.

Chorus of Nobles, etc.

SOPRANO.
Up with the ban - ner, and down with the

TENOR.
With the ban - ner, down with the

BASS.
With the ban - ner, down with the

slave Who shall dare to dis - pute the

slave Who shall dare dis - pute the

slave Who shall dare dis - pute the

right, Wher - ev - er its folds in their glo - ry wave, Of the

right, Wher - ev - er its folds in their glo - ry wave, Of the

right, Wher - ev - er its folds in their glo - ry wave, Of the

Aus - trian Ea - gle's flight, of the Aus - trian Ea - gle's flight,

Aus - trian Ea - gle's flight, of the Aus - trian Ea - gle's flight,

Aus - trian Ea - gle's flight, of the Aus - trian Ea - gle's flight,

of the Aus - trian Ea - gle's flight.

of the Aus - trian Ea - gle's flight.

of the Aus - trian Ea - gle's flight.

(After they have fixed the flag, they all come forward.)

Its pin - ion flies Free in the

Its pin - ion flies Free in the

Its pin - ion flies Free in the

Più mosso.

skies As that of the air - y

skies As that of the air - y

skies As that of the air - y

20

16118

(At the end of the Chorus, Count Arnheim and Florestein enter from château, S. E. L., followed by various neighboring Nobles, Pages, Huntsmen, etc., and his child, Arline, attended by Buda, etc.)

"A Soldier's Life."
Cavatina.

24

glen,
Where the hunt-er's belt-ed men

glen,
Where the hunt-er's belt-ed men

glen,
Where the hunt-er's belt-ed men

With bu-gles shake the air!

With bu-gles shake the air!

With bu-gles shake the air!

(The Count, after bowing to his friends, sees Arline, and takes her in his arms.)
Count.

Ah; who can tell, save he who feels The care a

pa-rent's love re-veals, How dear, fond thing, thou art To

this lone, wi-dow'd heart, to this lone heart! Ah, who can

tell the care, the care a pa-rent's love re-veals; how

rall.

dear, fond thing, thou art to this lone, wi-dow'd

heart!

Chorus of Hunters and Nobles.
SOPRANO and ALTO.

A-way to hill and glen, Where the hunt-er's

TENOR.

A- -way to hill and glen,

BASS.

A-way to hill and glen, Where the hunt-er's

A - way to the hills,

a tempo   *ff*

28

16118

30

16118

c. a - way,_____ a - way!

a - - way,

way, now to hill and glen a - way, a - way!

way, now to hill and glen a - way, a - way!

way, now to hill and glen a - way, a - way!

(During this, a retainer brings down [R.] a rifle to Florestein, who puts it away from him. Count Arnheim exit in château. Nobles and Hunters ascend rocks and exeunt. Arline petitions Buda to let her accompany them, and goes off by a footpath, at side of rocks, with her and Florestein.)

Melodramatic Music.

Allegro agitato.

(Enter Thaddeus, breathless and exhausted, in a state of great alarm.)

Thaddeus [spoken].— A guard of Austrian soldiers are on my track, and I can no longer elude their vigilance. An exile from my wretched country, now a prey to the inveterate invader, my only hope is in some friendly shelter. (Sees the statue of the Emperor.) Ah! that tells me I am here on the very threshold of our enemies!

"'Tis sad to leave our Fatherland."
Recitative and Aria.

T. well,___ To wander on a stranger strand, Where friends but sel - dom

dwell; Yet, hard as are such ills to bear, And deep - ly tho' they

smart, Their pangs are light to those who are The or - phans of the

heart!___ 'Tis sad to leave our Fa - ther-land, And friends we there lov'd

well,___ To wan-der on a stranger strand, Where friends but sel - dom

be, No lan - guage, no lan - guage

can express, how dear That heart would be to me, would be to me! O

Heav'n, O Heav'n! 'Tis sad to leave our Fa - ther - land, And

friends we there lov'd well, _____ To wander on a stranger strand, Where

friends but sel - dom dwell; Yet, hard as are such ills to bear, And

deep - ly tho' they smart, Their pangs are light to those who are The

or - phans of the heart!__ 'Tis hard to leave our Fa - ther - land, And

friends we there lov'd well,__ To wander on a stranger strand, Where

friends but sel - - dom dwell, where friends but sel - dom dwell, where

friends but sel - dom dwell, where friends but sel - dom dwell, where friends,

strascinando la voce

where___ friends but sel - dom dwell!

colla voce

(At the end of song, a troop of Gipsies, headed by Devilshoof, their leader, suddenly appear [R.] and are about to seize and rob Thaddeus, but presuming by his dress that he is a soldier, they stop and examine him.)

"In the Gipsy's Life."

Gipsy Chorus.

Thaddeus (aside). The sight of these wanderers has inspired me with a project. (To Devilshoof.) Your manner and habit please me. I should like to join your band. I am young, strong, and have, I hope, plenty of courage.

Devilshoof. Who are you?

Thad. One without money, without home, and without hope.

Dev. You're just the fellow for us, then!

Gipsy (who is on the look-out on rock, R.). Soldiers are coming this way.

Thad. 'Tis I they are in search of.

Dev. Indeed! then they'll be cunning if they find you.

(March begins.)

(In a moment they strip the soldier's dress off Thaddeus, and as they are putting a Gipsy's frock, &c., over him, a roll of parchment, with seal attached, falls at the feet of Devilshoof, who seizes it.)

Dev. What's this?

Thad. My commission! It is the only thing I possess on earth, and I will never part with it.

(Snatches it, conceals it in his bosom, and has just time to mix himself with the Gipsies, when a body of the Emperor's soldiers enter in pursuit.)

Officer (scrutinizing Gipsies). Have you seen any one pass this way — any stranger?

Dev. No one — stay — yes, a young Polish soldier ran by just now, and passed up those rocks.

Officer. That's he — thanks, friend! Forward!

(Exeunt soldiers up rocks.)

March of the Austrian Soldiers.

16118

D. C. **pp** till Soldiers go off, then segue Duet.

"Comrade, your Hand."

Duet with Chorus.

48

store, ____ no_ time_ can e'er re - store.

SOPRANO.

ALTO and TENOR.

In the Gipsy's life you read ____ The

BASS.

In the Gipsy's life you read ____ The

In the Gipsy's life you read ____ The

life that all would like to lead, ____ In the Gipsy's life you read The life that

life that all would like to lead, ____ In the Gipsy's life you read The life that

life that all would like to lead, ____ In the Gipsy's life you read The life that

Thaddeus.

Devilshoof.

My wants are few.

Want we ne'er

all would like to _ lead.

all would like to lead.

all would like to lead.

Più mosso.

Segue.

(Loud shouts and alarms are heard, which become more and more distinct, when a body of huntsmen are seen to cross a chasm in the rocks which is bridged by a fallen tree, &c., and exeunt by the path on which Arline, &c., went off.)

Melodramatic Music.

(Alarms continue, when Florestein rushes in, apparently frightened to death.)

"Is no succor near at hand?"
(Original key B minor.)

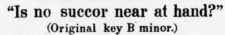

Aria.

Florestein.

Is no succor near at hand? For my in - - tel-lect so reels, I am
doubtful if I stand On my head_____ or on my heels; No
gentle-man, it's ver-y clear,_____ Such a shock should ev - er know; When I
once be-come a peer,_____ They shall not treat me so; No
gentle-man, it's ver-y clear, Such a shock_____ should ev - er know, And when

once I become a peer, They shall _____ not treat me so, no,_____

___ they shall not treat me so, no,_____ they shall not treat me

so! Then let

ev - er - y vas - sal arm, For my thanks_____ he well de - serves, Who from

this state, this state of a - larm Will protect_____ my shat - ter'd nerves! To

think that one unus'd to fear___ Such a fright should ev - er know! When I

once be - come a peer,___ They shall not treat_ me so! No

gentle-man, it's ver-y clear, Such a shock___ should ev - er know, And when

once I become a peer, They shall___ not treat me so, no,___

_ they shall not treat me so, no,___ they shall not

treat me so!

Segue

(At the end of song, Thaddeus and Peasantry rush in, the latter evincing the greatest alarm and terror.)

Melodramatic Music.

Allegro vivace.

Thaddeus. What means this alarm?
Peasant. The Count's child and her attendant have
  been attacked by an infuriated animal, and are
  probably killed ere this!
Thaddeus. What do I hear?

[Melodramatic Music begins.]

(He perceives the rifle that Florestein has left on the
stage, utters an exclamation, seizes it, runs up the
rocks, aims, fires, and instantly rushes off. The
discharge of the rifle, and the alarm of the Peasantry, bring Count Arnheim and his party to the
spot. Devilshoof enters at one side, at the same
time, watching.)

Melodramatic Music.

Count. Whence proceed these sounds of fear, and where is my darling child? [Melodramatic Music.] (All maintain a painful silence, when Thaddeus rushes in, conveying Arline, who is wounded in the arm, and seems faint.)

Melodramatic Music.

64

Buda (falling at the Count's feet). We were pursued by the wild deer they were chasing, and, but for the bravery of this young man (pointing to Thaddeus), the life of your child would have been sacrificed.

Count (clasping his child in his arms). Praised be Providence! her life is saved, for she is all that renders mine happy. (Looking at her arm, then addressing Buda.) Let her wound have every attention, though it presents no sign of danger.

(Buda goes into the castle with Arline, and Count Arnheim advances to Thaddeus.)

Stranger, accept the hand of one who, however different from you in station, can never sufficiently thank you for the service you have rendered him.

Devilshoof (aside). First to serve, and then be thanked by the persecutor of his country. The fellow's mad!

Count. I trust you will remain, and join the festivities we are about to indulge in; and 'twill gra-

tify me to hear how I can be useful to you.

Thaddeus. I thank your lordship; but —

Count (to the Nobles). Pray, my friends, join your entreaties to mine.

(Here the Nobles all surround the Count and Thaddeus; and Florestein, coming up to him, says —)

Flor. I am extremely obliged to you for not shooting me as well as my little cousin — and I beg you'll—aw—stay— (aside) A very common sort of personage, apparently.

Thad. (to the Count). Be it as your lordship wishes.

Count. Then be seated, friends, and let the fête begin.

(They all seat themselves at the tables which have previously been laid opposite the Castle. Thaddeus takes his seat at the farther end, Florestein occupying a prominent position. When they are seated, a variety of dances are introduced, during which Buda is seen at one of the windows holding on her knee the child, whose arm is bound up. At the termination of the dancing, the Count rises.)

Waltz.

Tempo di valse.

Più mosso.

Count (rising). I ask you to pledge but once, and that is, to the health and long life to your Emperor.

(Here the guests fill their glasses, rise, and turning towards the statue of the Emperor, drink, while the Peasantry surround it respectfully. Thaddeus alone keeps his seat, on perceiving which, Florestein goes up to the Count and points it out to him.)

Florestein. Your new acquaintance, my dear uncle, is not overburdened with politeness or loyalty, for he neither fills his glass, nor fulfils your wishes.

Count (filling a glass and going up to Thaddeus). I challenge you to empty this to the health of our Emperor.

Thaddeus (taking the glass). I accept the challenge, and thus I empty the goblet.

(Goes up to the statue and throws down the glass with the utmost contempt. A general burst of indignation follows.)

Chorus of Guests, who rise, draw their swords, and rush towards Thaddeus.

"Down with the daring slave."
Finale to Act I.

70

16118

of gold to Thaddeus)

(Devilshoof rushes in,)

C. ser - vice you did me re - quite!

Devilshoof (taking the hand of Thaddeus). (to Count)

D. Where's the hand will dare to touch A hair of him I prize so much? The

D. pulse of pride you boast, within, with - in me beats as high;

D. You and your titled host, Proud lord, proud lord, I do de - fy!

Florestein (aside, with a glass in one hand, and a leg of a bird in the other).

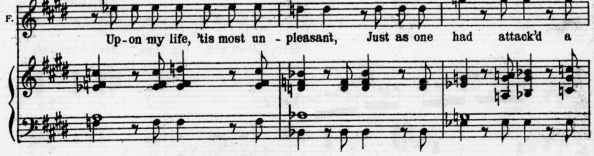

F. Up-on my life, 'tis most un - pleasant, Just as one had attack'd a

(Thaddeus, who has taken up the purse, and seeing himself and Devilshoof surrounded by the Nobles and Guests, throws the purse at the Count's feet.)

(Devilshoof, defending Thaddeus, retreats, pressed upon by the nobles. guests, &c., when the count orders a party of his retainers to divide them; they seize Devilshoof, and take him towards the Castle.)

Devilshoof.

Stand back, ye cra - ven

slave who would, who would our fu - ry brave.

slave who would, who would our fu - ry brave.

slave who would, who would our fu - ry brave.

f

things! He who ob - structs our path Up-

on his rash - ness brings The ven - geance of my

wrath!

Down with the slave! down with the slave! Seize him and

Down with the slave! down with the slave! Seize him and

Down with the slave! down with the slave! Seize him and

p   *pp*

16118

bind him, and there let him find Es-cape from those walls bet-ter men have con-

bind him, and there let him find Es-cape from those walls bet-ter men have con-

bind him, and there let him find Es-cape from those walls bet-ter men have con-

fin'd, there let him find an es-cape from those walls bet-ter men have con-

fin'd, there let him find an es-cape from those walls bet-ter men have con-

fin'd, there let him find an es-cape from those walls bet-ter men have con-

Devilshoof (as they are dragging him off).

Tho' mesh'd by num - bers in the yoke Of

fin'd!

fin'd!

fin'd!

(Devilshoof is dragged off into the castle; the Count, Nobles, etc., reseat themselves, when other dances are introduced, and the festival continues. Buda is seen to leave the window at which she has been seated with Arline, and she enters and converses with the Count. In the midst of the most joyous movements of the dance, Devilshoof is seen descending from the roof of the castle, until he reaches the window of Arline's chamber, into which he enters, and seizing Arline, continues his descent and steals off towards the rocks in the rear. Buda then enters the castle, and in a minute afterwards the festivities are interrupted by violent shrieking; the window is thrown open, and Buda, pale, and with dishevelled hair, signifies by her gestures that Arline has disappeared.)

Galop.

Allegro vivace.

"What sounds break on the ear?"

Finale continued.

With a - go - niz - ing tone, my child! that word a - lone Bursts in up - on

(Count and Nobles dash into the castle. A general movement of all — some are seen at the window of Arline's chamber signifying that she is gone.)

my heart!

Be ev - 'ry hand pre - par'd —
Be ev - 'ry hand pre - par'd —
Be ev - 'ry hand pre - par'd

Their liege lord's halls to guard, And with de -
Their liege lord's halls to guard, And with de -
Their liege lord's halls to guard, And with de -

Florestein (kneeling, and appearing greatly alarmed).

vo - tion's bond, All ties, all ties be - yond —

Ah! what with danc - ing, scream - ing,

fighting, One real - ly is a shock - ing

plight in; It puz - zles quite one's

wit To find a place to pick a bit.

(The Count rushes from the castle, dragging Buda and followed by Nobles. Buda, trembling, falls on her knees.)

Count.

Wretch! mon - ster! give me back the trea - sure of my soul, the trea - sure of __ my soul!

Go — all — the spoil - er's foot - steps track, That treasur'd prize who stole; Go — all — the spoil - er's foot - steps track, That treasur'd prize __ who

*)On the stage this prayer is sung without instrumental accompaniment.

Vouch-safe to lend an ear To the grief of the wail - er, Cut short the dark ca-

Vouch-safe to lend an ear To the grief of the wail - er, Cut short the dark ca-

Vouch-safe to lend an ear To the grief of the wail - er, Cut short the dark ca-

Vouch-safe to lend an ear To the grief of the wail - er, Cut short the dark ca-

reer Of the ruth-less as-sail - er, of the ruthless as-sail - er,

reer Of the ruth-less as - sail - er, of the ruthless as - sail - er,

reer Of the ruth-less as -sail - er, of the ruthless as - sail - er,

reer Of the ruth-less as - sail - er, of the ruthless as - sail - er,

Cut short the dark ca - reer, the dark ca-reer Of the ruth-less as - sail - er,

Cut short the dark ca - reer Of the ruth-less as - sail - er,

Cut short the dark ca - reer Of the ruth-less as - sail - er,

Cut short the dark ca - reer Of the ruth-less as - sail - er,

Cut short the dark ca - reer Of the ruth-less as - sail - er,

Cut short the dark ca - reer Of _ the ruthless assail - - - er.

Of _ the ruthless as-sail - - - er.

Of _ the ruthless as-sail - - - er.

Cut short the dark ca - reer Of _ the ruthless as-sail - - - er.

Allegro.

(During the prayer, Devilshoof is seen climbing up the rocks with Arline in his arms.)

(At the most animated part of the Chorus, bodies of Gentry, Retainers, Servants, &c., are seen rushing towards the rocks, and over every part, in pursuit of Devilshoof, who, perceiving his situation, knocks away, the moment he has crossed it, the trunk of the tree which serves as a bridge between the two rocks, and thus bars their passage. Count Arnheim in his distraction is about to throw himself into the gulf — he is held back by attendants, into whose arms he falls senseless. Some are in attitude of prayer — others menace Devilshoof, who, folding Arline in his large cloak, disappears in the depths of the forest.

"Follow, follow with heart and with arm."

Chorus.

Più mosso.

Fol - low and save the pride of Arn - heim's

Fol - low and save the pride of Arn - heim's

Fol - low and save the pride of Arn - heim's

line, Where all its hopes, its hopes en - twine.

line, Where all its hopes, its hopes en - twine.

line, Where all its hopes, its hopes en - twine.

End of Act I.

Act II.

Note.— Twelve years are supposed to elapse between the First and Second Acts.

Scene I. Street in Presburg, by moonlight. Tent of the Queen of the Gipsies, large curtains at the back; it is lighted by a lamp. On the opposite side of the stage are houses, one of which, an hotel, is lighted up. Arline is discovered asleep on a tiger's skin; Thaddeus is watching over her. As the curtain rises, a patrol of the city guard marches by, and as soon as they are gone off, Devilshoof and a party of Gipsies, wrapped in cloaks, suddenly appear.

"Silence, the Lady Moon."
Introduction.

steep. Watch here! till each to his home Shall reel on his doubtful

way. Watch here! watch here! and the gob-let's foam Will make

each an ea-sy prey. Si - lence! this way, this way, this way, this

way, silence, this way, this way,___

Chorus.

Si - - lence, si-lence, this way, this way,___ si - - lence,

Si - - lence, si-lence, this way, this way,___ si - -

Si - - lence, si-lence, this way, this way,___ si - -

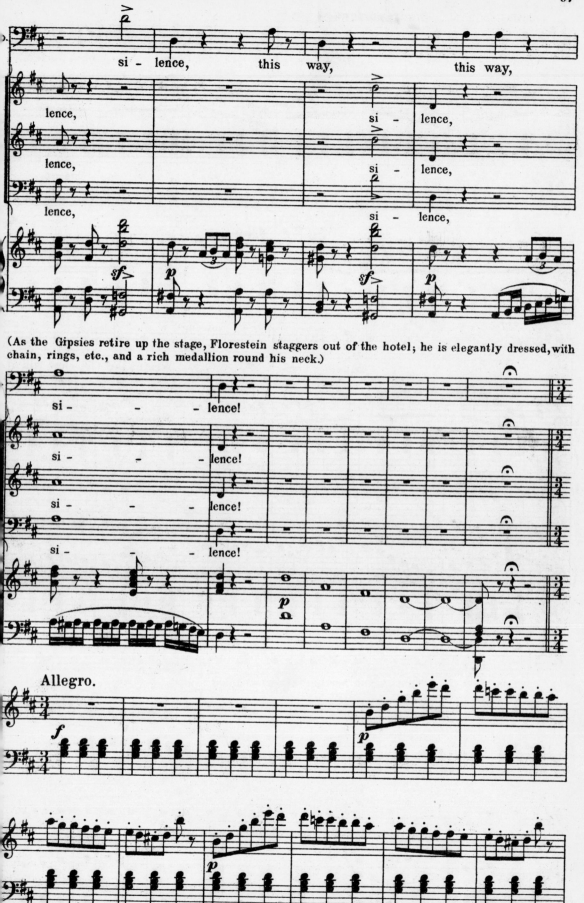

(As the Gipsies retire up the stage, Florestein staggers out of the hotel; he is elegantly dressed, with chain, rings, etc., and a rich medallion round his neck.)

Allegro.

Florestein (drunk). *quasi parlando*

Wine! wine! if I am heir To the Count, my un – cle's, line, Wine! (hiccup) Wine! (hiccup) Where's the fel – low will dare To re – fuse his ne – –phew wine, to re-fuse his nephew wine? (hiccup) That moon there, star-ing me on my way, Can't be as mod-est as peo – ple say, For meet whom she will, and in what-ev-er spot, She

(The Gipsies have by this time advanced, and Devilshoof goes politely up to Flor.)

Dev. (to Flor., bowing).

oft - en looks on at what she ought not.

My

ear caught not the clock's last chime, And might I beg to

p sempre stacc.

ask the time?

Florestein (reels, recovers a little, and after eyeing Devils-
(aside)

(If the bot - tle has pre-vail'd, Yet when-

hoof).

ev - er I'm as-sail'd, Tho' there may be nothing in it, I am so - ber'd

(to Devilshoof)

in a minute.) You are real - ly so po - lite,

16118

(pulling out his watch)

(Devilshoof takes the watch and puts it in his fob)

That _ 'tis late in-to the night _ Might I beg to

Dev. (taking from Florestein his rings, chain, and the rich medallion).

ask _ I am real - ly griev'd to see A-ny one in such a state,

And glad-ly will take the great-est care Of the rings and chains you

Flor. (drawing his sword).

chance to wear. What I thought was po - lite-ness, is down-right theft, And at

this rate I soon shall have no - thing left.

(At a sign from Devilshoof the Gipsies instantly surround Florestein, and take every valuable from him

(During the chorus, Devilshoof makes off with the medallion, and the others are dividing the rest of the spoil, when a female appears in the midst of them, drops her cloak, and discovers their Queen. The Gipsies appear stupefied.)

16118

Recit. **Queen.**

To him, from whom you stole, Surren-der back the whole.

The Gipsies return the different things to Florestein.

Florestein (trembling and looking over the things).

Thanks, Ma-dam, La-dy, but

Tempo I.

pp

pp staccato

might I re-quest A me-dal-lion in di-a-monds, worth all the

rest?

Chorus (at a sign from the Queen, who seems to command its restitution).

On our chief-tain's share we ne'er en-croach, And he fled with the

On our chief-tain's share we ne'er en-croach, And he fled with the

On our chief-tain's share we ne'er en-croach, And he fled with the

prize at your ap–proach, he fled with the

prize at your ap–proach, he fled with the

prize at your ap–proach, he fled with the

prize at your ap – – proach.

prize at your ap – – proach.

prize at your ap – – proach.

Tempo I.

Queen (to Florestein).

Flor. (trembling).

Be your safe – ty my care. I'm in precious hands.

Queen (to Gipsies).

Fol – low, and list to your Queen's____ com – mands.

16118

Queen.

Come,   come, come!

list, we list to our Queen's com - mands, yes, yes, yes,

list, we list to our Queen's com - mands, yes, yes, yes,

list, we list to our Queen's com - mands, yes, yes, yes,

Queen.

fol - - low!

fol - - low!

fol - - low!

(Exit Queen, holding Florestein, all of a tremble, with one hand, and beckoning the Gipsies to follow, with the other.)

Moderato.

(Exeunt omnes.)

(As soon as they have gone off, Arline, who has been awakened by the noise, comes from the tent, followed by Thaddeus.

Arline. Where have I been wandering in my sleep? and what curious noise awoke me from its pleasant dream? Ah, Thaddeus, would you not like to know my dream? Well, I will tell it you.

"I dreamt that I dwelt in marble halls."

Andantino.   **Romance.**

110 (At the end of the romance Thaddeus press‒ es Arline to his heart.)

Arline. And do you love me still?

Thaddeus. More than life itself.

Arline. Yet is there a mystery between our affec‒ tions and their happiness that I would fain un ravel (pointing to her arm). The mark on this arm, which I have seen you so often contem‒ plate, is the key to that mystery. By the love you say you bear me, solve it.

"The wound upon thine arm."
Duet.

Thaddeus (taking her hand and pointing to the mark).

The wound___ up‒on thine arm, Whose mark___ thro' life 'twill be, In sav‒ing thee from great‒ ‒er__ harm Was there trans‒fix'd by me.

Arline. By thee?

Thaddeus. Ere on thy gen‒tle head Thy sixth sun had its radiance

shed, A wild deer, who had lain at bay, Pursued by

Arline. Thadd.

hunt - ers cross'd thy way. Well? By slaying him I res - cued

Arline. Thadd.

thee. Yes! And in his death-throe's a - go - ny, Thy tender form, by his ant - ler

Arline.

gor'd, This humble arm to thy home re-stor'd. Strange

feel - ings move this breast, It nev - er knew be - fore, And bid me

Larghetto cantabile.

mezza voce   Thadd.

Arline.

"What is the spell hath yet effaced."

16118

Tempo I.

Thaddeus.

love's con - fid - ing_ breast? And yet few_spells have e'er ef-fac'd The

first fond lines that love hath trac'd, And af - ter - years have but im-prest More

deep in love's confid - ing breast! And yet few_spells have e'er ef-fac'd The

first fond lines that love hath trac'd, And_ af - ter - years have but im-prest More

deep in love's confid - ing breast, more_deep in_ love's con - fid - ing_

Tempo I.

dolce

A. What is_ the spell hath yet ef-fac'd The

T. *dolce* What is_ the spell hath yet ef-fac'd The

Tempo I.

pp stacc.

A. first fond lines that love hath trac'd, And af - ter - years have

T. first fond lines that love hath trac'd, And af - ter - years have

A. but im - prest More deep in love's con-fid - ing breast?

T. but im - prest More deep in love's con-fid - ing breast?

A. *f* What is_ the spell hath yet ef-fac'd The first fond lines that

T. *f* What is_ the spell hath yet ef-fac'd The first fond lines that

A. fid - ing breast, more deep in love's con -

T. fid - ing breast, more deep in love's con -

A. fid - ing breast, in love's con - fid - ing breast, in

T. fid - ing breast, in love's con - fid - ing breast, in

A. love's con - fid - ing breast!

T. love's con - fid - ing breast!

ff

(At the end of the duet, Thaddeus throws himself, in an ecstasy, at the feet of Arline, and is bathing her hand with kisses, when the back curtains of the tent are withdrawn, and the Queen appears, pale and trembling with passion. She advances towards Arline, and pointing to Thaddeus —)

Queen. And dare you aspire to the love of him who possesses the heart of your queen?

Arline. I possess *his* heart, and will yield the possession to no one. He is the savior of my life, and the only friend I have in all the tribe: he has sworn how much he loves me.

Queen. Loves you?

(Trumpet sounds twice, then segue.)

Arline. Yes; let him speak for himself, and choose between us.

Queen. Be it so.

(Thaddeus, who has been anxiously watching the two, here runs and embraces Arline. She surveys the Queen with an air of triumph.)

Arline (to the Queen). I made no idle boast. (Then to Thaddeus —) Summon our comrades hither.

(The Queen is standing in the centre, while Thaddeus calls the Gipsies together, who enter on all sides and surround the Queen, and appear to ask what is going on.)

"Happy and light of heart."
Recitative and Chorus.

D. it perchance may be as well To set them both, to set them both by the ears.) As

D. Queen of our tribe, 'tis yours by__ right, The hands of those you rule to u - nite.

(to Queen, who draws back and hesitates)

Chorus.

In love and truth by__ thee Their hands u - nit - ed__ be.

In love and truth by thee Their hands u - nit - ed be.

In love and truth by thee Their hands u - nit - ed be.

Meno mosso, *quasi a piacere.*

Queen (haughtily advancing, and taking the hands of Arline and Thaddeus).

Q. Hand to hand, heart to heart, Who shall those I've u -

Q. nit - ed part? who shall those I have mat-ed part? By the

+)This is sung on the stage without accompaniment.

pose, happy and light, who faith re-pose, who in each

pose, happy and light, who faith re-pose, who in each

pose, happy and light, who faith re-pose, who in each

oth — — er faith re-pose, who faith re-pose.

oth — — er faith re-pose, who faith re-pose.

oth — — er faith re-pose, who faith re-pose.

(Chorus lie down, assuming picturesque attitudes. Queen comes forward; then segue Ballad.)

"Bliss for ever past."
Ballad.

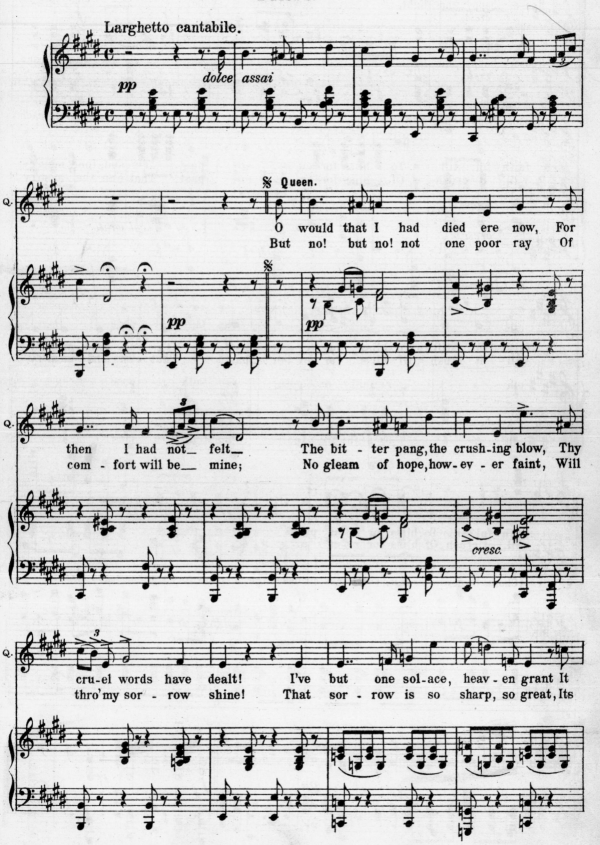

(During this scene the stage has been growing somewhat lighter. A Gipsy enters.)
Gipsy. Morning is beginning to dawn, and crowds
of people are already flocking towards the fair:
the sports begin with daylight.

Queen. Summon the rest of the tribe, and meet
me forthwith in the public square. (To Devilshoof.) Do you remain to bear my further orders.
(Exeunt Thaddeus and Arline, hand in hand, followed by the other Gipsies repeating chorus.)

Chorus.

dim.

in the Gip-sy's life you read the life that all would like to

dim.

in the Gip-sy's life you read the life that all would like to

dim.

in the Gip-sy's life you read the life that all would like to

dim.

lead, *dim.* in the Gip-sy's life you read the life that all would

dim.

lead, in the Gip-sy's life you read the life that all would

dim.

lead, in the Gip-sy's life you read the life that all would

dim.

like to lead._____

like to lead._____

like to lead._____

Segue Duet

"This is thy deed."
Duet.

jew - el with which thou hast dared to deck Thy fore - doom'd neck, Answer

me _ where didst thou get it? where? 'Twas entrusted to my

Devilshoof.

care. **Queen.** This ver - y night, on this ver - y

spot, Thy soul for once its fears for - got, A drunk - en gal -

liard who cross'd thy way Be - came thy prey. (Fiend -

Devilshoof (aside).

do thy high be - hest. *f* (aside) (The

Queen.

Now de - part, and join the rest,

wrongs we forgive not and cannot forget, Will vengeance more sharply whet, the

(aside)

now de - part and join the rest! (The

wrongs we forgive not and cannot forget, will vengeance more sharply whet, the

wrongs we forgive not and can - not forget, will vengeance more sharply whet, the

wrongs we forgive not and can - not forget, will vengeance more sharply whet, the

ven - - geance more sharp - ly

cresc.

Be -

whet,_____ more sharp - - ly

(Exeunt Queen and Devilshoof at opposite sides.)

gone!

whet!)

(segue when scene changes)

a tempo

Scene II. — Another street in Presburg. Daylight.

"Come with the Gipsy bride."
Romance with Chorus.

N.B. If sung without the Chorus, the small notes in the accompaniment should be played as a substitute for the voices.

(Enter Arline, in a fanciful dress, followed by a troop of Gipsies. She has a tambourine in her hand.)

*) On the stage, the first and the last eight measures of Chorus are sung without accompaniment.

Arline.

Come with the Gip-sy bride, Where souls as light pre-side! Life can give nothing be-

yond One heart ___ you know to be fond, ___ Wealth with its hoards cannot buy ___ The

peace content can sup-ply, ___ Wealth with its hoards cannot buy ___ The peace content can sup-

rallent. a piacere

ply, ___ And rank in its halls can-not find ___ The calm of a hap-py

colla voce

rall.

mind, And rank in its halls can-not find The calm of a hap-py mind.

col canto

Arline.

Love is the first thing to clasp, But if _____ he es-cape your grasp,

Friend-ship will then be at hand, In the young _____ rogue's place to

stand, Hope will then be no-thing loath _____ To

point out the way to both, Hope will then be no-thing

loath _____ To point out the way to both. _____

(Exit Arline, followed by the Gipsies)

Scene III. A grand Fair in the public Platz (Square) of Presburg. On one side a large hotel, over which is inscribed "The Hall of Justice." Various groups of Gentry, Soldiers, Citizens, and Peasantry cover the stage. Foreign shops are seen in various parts, curious Rope-dancers, Showmen, Waxwork, a Quack Doctor, Exhibitions, etc. etc., are dispersed here and there. Flags hung out of the windows, and ringing of bells, enliven the scene.

March.

(When the scene changes.)

molto marcato

(Segue Fair-Scene.)

"Life itself is, at the best."

The Fair-Scene.

Allegro.

SOPRANO and ALTO.

Life it - self is, at the best, One scene in

TENOR.

Life it - self is, at the best, One scene in

BASS.

mask of fol - ly drest; And there is no

mask of fol - ly drest; And there is no

BASS.

To these symbols of life your voic-es swell, Vive la masque, et vive la ba-ga-telle!

Vive la masque, vive la masque, vive la masque, et vive la ba-ga-telle!

Full Chorus.

Life it - self is, at the best, One scene in

Life it - self is, at the best, One scene in

Life it - self is, at the best, One scene in

mask of fol - ly drest, Life it - self is,

mask of fol - ly drest, Life it - self is,

mask of fol - ly drest, Life it - self is,

(Quack Doctor's horn; **Allegro assai.** *)

numbers rush towards him.)

(At the end of the Chorus, and during the Symphony, a movement is perceived at the further end of the Platz, which is followed by the entrance of a double party of men Gipsies, headed by Devilshoof and Thaddeus, who force a passage down the centre of the stage, which they occupy; they then open their ranks, when another file of female Gipsies, headed by their Queen and Arline, pass between them. Florestein and a party are seen watching them with great curiosity.)

Allegro assai.

*) These 11 measures are now omitted in performance.

"From the valleys and hills."

Allegro assai.   *) Quartet.

*) On the stage this Quartet is sung without accompaniment.

(During this, some of the Gipsies have been enacting characteristic dances, when Arline, carrying a flower-basket in her hand, glides round to the assembled company and sits down.)

Allegro ma non troppo.

Arline.   (to a lady)

Sir Knight and la - dy, list - en! That bright eye seems to glist - en

As if his trust - ed tale Did o'er thy sense pre - vail!

(to another, pointing to her heart)

Pret - ty   maid - en, pray, take care, take care,

Love is mak - ing hav - oc there,

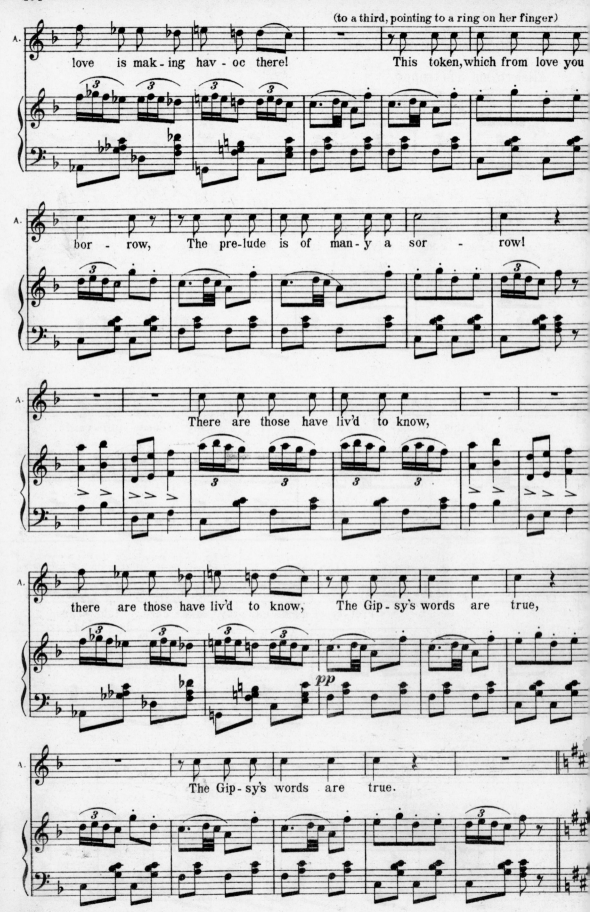

(to a third, pointing to a ring on her finger)

love is mak - ing hav - oc there! This token, which from love you

bor - row, The pre-lude is of man - y a sor - row!

There are those have liv'd to know,

there are those have liv'd to know, The Gip - sy's words are true,

The Gip - sy's words are true.

Chorus (as the dance of Gipsies continues).

Life it - self is, at the best, One scene in

Life it - self is, at the best, One scene in

Life it - self is, at the best, One scene in

mask of fol - ly drest, Life it - self is,

mask of fol - ly drest, Life it - self is,

mask of fol - ly drest, Life it - self is,

at the best, One scene in mask of fol - ly

at the best, One scene in mask of fol - ly

at the best, One scene in mask of fol - ly

(At the end of the dance and chorus, Count Arnheim and some Officers of State enter; his hair has become grey, his step is slow, and his appearance is that of sorrow. He is accosted by Florestein.)

Florestein. My dear uncle, it delights me to see you amongst us, and here is a little Gipsy girl that would delight you still more, (aside) if you had my blood in your veins; she's positively a charming creature.

Count. I have lost the taste of joy, and the sight of youth and beauty recalls to my memory that treasure of both, my loved and lost Arline.

(He gazes attentively at Arline, sighs heavily, then exit with his retinue into the Hall of Justice.)

Flor. (to a party of his friends). It's no use restraining me—I'm positively smitten. (Breaks from them and goes up to Arline.) Fair creature, your manner has enchanted me, and I would take a lesson from you.

Arline. In politeness, sir? By all means! To begin, then, whenever you address a lady, take your hat off.

Flor. Very smart, (with a titter) 'pon my word, very smart. Your naïveté only increases the feelings of admiration and devotion which a too susceptible heart—

Arline (bursting out laughing). Ha! ha! ha!

Flor. Your indifference will drive me to despair.

Arline. Will it really?

Flor. Do not mock me, but pity my too susceptible nature, and let me print one kiss upon—

(Here Arline gives him a violent slap on the face; the Queen, who has gone up the stage with Thaddeus, now brings him on one side and points out the situation of Arline and Florestein—he is about to rush upon Florestein just as Arline has slapped his face; so that as Flor. turns round, he finds himself between the two, and both are laughing in his face.)

Queen (eyeing Florestein). It is the very person from whom they stole the trinkets I made them give back again. (Taking the medallion from her bosom.) This, too, is his, and now my project thrives. (Florestein turns up the stage to join his party, and the Queen crosses to Arline.) You have acted well your part, and thus your Queen rewards you. (Places the medallion round her neck.) Forget not the hand that gave it.

Arline (kneeling, and kissing the Queen's hand). Let this bespeak my gratitude.

Queen. And now let our tribe depart.

Gipsy March.

(The Gipsies are all about to march off. Thaddeus and Arline bring up the rear of their body; as they are going off, Florenstein, who, with his friends, has been watching their departure, perceives his medallion on the neck of Arline—he breaks through the crowd, and stops her—she and Thaddeus come forward.)

Florestein. Though you treated me so lightly some moments past, you will not do so now. That medallion is mine; my friends here recognize it.

All. We do! we do! (Here Devilshoof is seen to steal off.)

Flor. And I accuse you of having stolen it.

Arline. Stolen! It was this instant given me by our Queen, and she is here to verify my words. (Arline runs about looking everywhere for the Queen.)

Flor. That's an everyday sort of subterfuge. (To the crowd.) Worthy people and friends, that medallion on her neck belongs to me, and I accuse her or her accomplices of having robbed me.

"Shame! Shame! Let us know the right."

Thaddeus (rushing before Arline to shield her).

He who a hand on her would lay,

Through my heart must force his way!

Chorus.

Tear them a - sun-der, but still pro - tect Un -

Tear them a - sun-der, but still pro - tect Un -

Tear them a - sun-der, but still pro - tect Un -

til they can prove what they sus -

til they can prove what they sus -

til they can prove what they sus -

(Florestein, who has, during this movement, entered the Hall of Justice, is now seen returning, followed by a strong guard, who file off on each side of the steps.)

Captain. To the Hall!

Chorus *unis.* To the Hall!

(Arline looks at him with great contempt; the Gipsies, perceiving her danger, range themselves around her. Thaddeus breaks from those who are holding him, and rushes up to her. Florestein has got behind the Captain of the Guard, who gives orders for his men to seize Arline, upon which the Gipsies draw their daggers. A conflict ensues, in which the Guard maintains possession of Arline. A body of the populace re-seize Thaddeus, and the Gipsies are routed.)

Thaddeus. Free me, or else the law Up-

Florestein. They who would brave the law, A-

Captain. They who would brave the law, A-

SOPRANO and ALTO. (People.) They who would brave the law, A-

TENOR. (Gipsies.) Why should we fear the law, Or

BASS. (Guards.) They who would brave the law, A-

cresc.

way, to the Hall, a - way, a - way, a -

way, to the Hall, a - way, a - way, a -

way, to the Hall, a - way, a - way, a -

way, to the Hall, a - way, a - way, a -

way, to the Hall, a - way, a - way, a -

way, a - way!

way, a - way!

way, a - way!

way, a - way!

way, a - way!

ff

(Arline is conducted by a file of the Guard, led by the Captain, and preceded by Florestein and his party, into the Hall of Justice; the people follow in a mass, while Thaddeus is detained by those who first seized him; and as Arline is going up the steps, the figure of the Queen is seen, in an attitude of triumph over her rival's fall.)

Scene IV. — Interior of Count Arnheim's apartment in the Hall of Justice — a view of the last Scene visible through one of the windows at the back. A full-length portrait of Arline, as she was in Act I, hangs on the wall; state chairs, etc. A elevation or dais on the O.P. side.

"The Heart bow'd down."
Recitative and Aria.

(Count Arnheim enters, thoughtful and dejected; he contemplates Arline's portrait, and wipes a tear from his eye.)

Count.

C. What-e'er the scenes the pre-sent hour calls forth be - fore__ the sight, They lose their

C. splen-dor when com - par'd with scenes of past__ de - light!

The heart bow'd down by weight of woe, To
The mind will, in its worst despair, Still

weak - est hope will cling, To thought and im - pulse
pon - der o'er the past, On mo - ments of de -

while they flow, That can no com - fort
light that were Too beau - ti - ful to

rall.

bring, that can, that can no com - fort
last, that were too beau - ti - ful, too beau - ti - ful to

string.

colla parte

bring, With those ex - cit - ing scenes will blend, O'er
last, To long de - part - ed years ex-tend Its

pp

(At the end of the song, a confused noise is heard outside, when the Captain of the Guard enters.)

Captain. A robbery has been committed, and the accused is now in the Hall awaiting the pleasure of your lordship, as chief magistrate of the city, for examination.

Count. Bring the parties before me.

(The Captain arranges the magisterial chair O.P., bows and exit.)

Anything to arouse me from these distracting thoughts, though the sole happiness I now enjoy is in the recollection of my long-lost child.

(Seats himself, when the doors are violently opened, and a mob of Citizens, Guards, and Gentry enter. Florestein, who is in the midst of them, instantly rushes up to the Count.)

Florestein. It is your lordship's nephew,—I, who have been robbed!

Count. Some folly of yours is for ever compromising my name and that of your family.

Flor. But I am in this instance the victim— I have been robbed, and there stands the culprit.

(Pointing to Arline, standing in the centre, pale and with dishevelled hair, but still haughty in her demeanor.)

Count (aside). 'Tis she I saw but now in the public square. That girl, so young, so beautiful, commit a robbery? Impossible!

Flor. She stole this medallion belonging to me— we found it upon her.

Count (addressing Arline). Can this be true?

Arline (looking contemptuously at Florestein, and turning with dignity to the Count). Heaven knows I am innocent, and if your lordship knew my heart, you would not deem me guilty.

Count (aside). Her words sink deep into my breast. Childless myself, I fain would spare the child of another. (To Florestein.) What proofs have you of this?

Flor. (pointing to his friends). My witnesses are here, who all can swear they saw it on her neck.

All. We can.

Count. Still does my mind misgive me. (To Arline, in a kind tone.) My wish is to establish your innocence—explain this matter to me, and without fear.

Arline. That medallion was given to me by the Queen of the tribe to which I belong. How it came into her possession, I know not. But a light breaks in upon me—I see it all—I chanced to incur her displeasure; and to revenge herself upon me, she has laid for me this shameless snare, into which I have innocently fallen, and of which I have become the victim.

(Hiding her face in her hands, and weeping.)

Count (with a struggle). I believe your tale, and from my heart I pity the inexperience which has led to the ruin of one, who seems above the grade of those she herds with; but in the fulfilment of duty I must compromise the feelings of nature, and I am forced to deliver you into the hands of Justice.

Arline (to the Count). To you, my earthly, to Him my heavenly Judge, I re-assert my innocence. I may be accused, but will not be degraded, and from the infamy with which I am unjustly threatened, thus I free myself.

(She draws a dagger from beneath her scarf, and is about to stab herself, when Count Arnheim rushes forward, seizes her arm, and wrests the dagger from her.)

"Hold! Hold!"
Finale to Act II.

break, nor re - u - nite the heart_ we break!

(takes Arline's hand, and suddenly perceives the scar on her arm)

What visions, what visions round me

marcato

rise, And cloud with the mists of the

past mine eyes? That mark! Those features! and thy

cresc.

(dragging Arline forward, and in great agitation)

youth! My ver - y life hangs on thy truth_ How came that

rest,__ to re-late   the rest.

(Here a tumult is heard, and Thaddeus, having escaped from those who confined him, breaks into the room, and rushes into the arms of Arline. The Count, on seeing him, reels back.   General excite-ment prevails.)

Count.

With the force of   fear and

Arline (approaching the Count and pointing to Thaddeus, who starts on beholding him).

hope My feel-ings have to cope!   'Tis   he____ the danger brav'd__ 'Tis

he   my   life who   saved, my life who saved!

Count (seizing Arline in his arms in a transport of joy).

Allegro agitato.

Mine own, my long - - - lost   child!   Oh, seek not

child! Oh, seek not to con - trol The frantic

joy, this wild De - li - rium of my

col canto

soul, this wild de - li - rium of _____ my _ soul, this wild de - li - rium

of my _ soul, of my _ soul! Arline. Speak,

(Count clasps Arline to his heart; kisses her head, hands and hair, shedding tears of joy. Arline, bewildered, starts from the Count and runs to Thaddeus.)

speak! this shak-en frame, _____ This doubt, this tor - ture,

marcato

Arline.

Thaddeus.

Florestein.

A. Heav'n, ah, _____ yes!

T. Heav'n, prais - ed be Heav'n!

F. Heav'n, ah, _____ yes!

C. Heav'n, prais - ed be Heav'n!

D. come, come, come, come, come!

Heav'n, prais - ed be Heav'n!

Heav'n, prais - ed be Heav'n!

decresc.

p

cresc.

f

ff

End of Act I

Scene I. A splendid saloon in the Castle of Count Arnheim. On the ground-floor, a large window at the back opening on the Park. On the side, the door of a small cabinet, doors at the back leading into spacious galleries.

Introduction.

Adagio.

(Enter Arline, elegantly dressed for a Ball.)

Arline. The past appears to me but a dream, from which I have at length aroused me. Yet my heart recalls enough to convince me it was all reality. When I think of the wandering life I led, my memory will revert to him who in every trial preserved its honor, who twice restored me to a father's arms, and at length to a father's home.

(Count Arnheim enters with Florestein. Arline runs into his arms.)

Count. Every moment you leave me is a moment of unhappiness. I am jealous of whatever divides us, short as may be the interval. On a night of so much joy, when so many friends are to assemble and participate in your father's delight, let me intercede for one you have too much cause to be angry with.

Arline (averting her head). The very sight of him disturbs me. (To the Count.) The wishes of my dear father I would cheerfully comply with, but my repugnance I cannot overcome.

Florestein (falling on his knee). Fair cousin, let me plead my own cause, and express the— aw—sorrow I really feel at having for an instant believed it possible — in fact, I never in reality —

(Enter a Servant.)

What the devil do you want at such a critical part of one's conversation?

(Servant crosses to the Count.)

Servant. The castle is filling with guests who inquire for your lordship. (Exit.)

Count (to Arline). Let us hasten to meet them, and afford me the joy of making you known to all.

Arline. Allow me but time to fortify myself for a ceremony I am a stranger to, and I will follow you.

Flor. That is but reasonable, uncle — I will live in hopes of my cousin's forgiveness, which can alone restore my—peace of mind. (Aside.) I shall positively expire if I don't lead off the first quadrille with her.

(Exeunt Count and Florestein.)

Arline. I am once more left to my thoughts, and all the deep regrets which accompany them; nothing can drive the recollection of Thaddeus from my mind, and the lonely life I led was to me far happier than the constrained one I now pass; and the graceful dress of the Gipsy girl becomes me more than all this gaudy apparel of nobility. (Going round the room to see if any one is watching.) Now no eye beholds me, I may at least indulge in a remembrance of the past.

(Melodramatic music.)

(Goes to the Cabinet O. P. and brings out her Gipsy dress.) The sight of this recalls the memory of happy days, and of him who made them happy.

(As she is contemplating the dress, the window at the back suddenly opens, and Devilshoof springs into the apartment.)

Arline (screaming). Ah! what seek you here with me?

Devilshoof. Hush! fear not; but be silent. I come to ask you to rejoin our tribe — we have never ceased to feel the loss of one liked more than all the rest.

Arline. Impossible! Leave me, I pray, and let me forget we have ever been acquainted.

Devilshoof. I have brought with me one who has, undoubtedly, greater powers of persuasion than I can pretend to.

(Here Thaddeus appears at the window, enters the room, and Arline, unable to restrain her feelings, rushes into his arms.)

Thaddeus. In the midst of so much luxury, so much wealth and grandeur, I thought you had forgotten me.

Arline. Forgotten you! Had I nothing else to remind me of you (pointing at her Gipsy dress), this would always speak to me of you. Forgotten you!

Thaddeus. The scenes in which you now move, may drive from your memory every trace of the past, and I only come to ask—to hope— that you will sometimes think upon me.

(Devilshoof goes up to the window, on the lookout.)

Melodramatic Music.

(Played when Arline takes out her Gipsy dress.)

Allegro moderato.

Arline. The sight of this recalls the memory of happy days, &c,

(Enter Devilshoof.)

"Then you'll remember me."
Cavatina.

When oth - er lips and oth - er hearts Their tales of love shall

tell, In language whose ex - cess im-parts The pow'r they feel so

well: There may, per - haps, in such a scene, Some

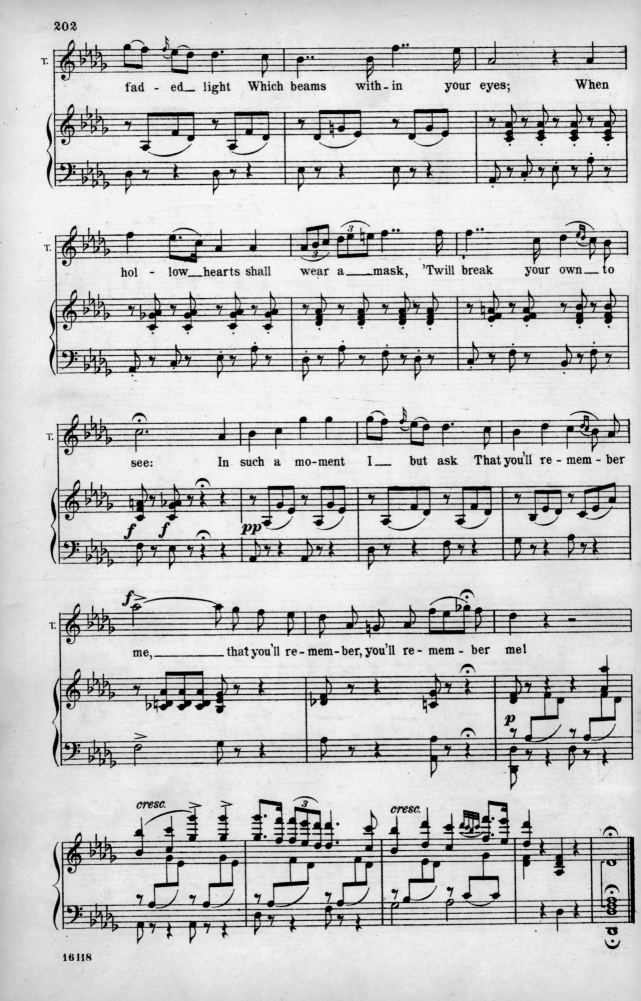

(At the end of the song, Arline goes up to Thaddeus, and with great emphasis says:)

Arline. Whatever may be our future lot, nothing should persuade you that I can ever cease to think of, ever cease to love you.

Thaddeus (overjoyed). My heart is overpowered with happiness. Yet, alas! 'tis but of short duration, for I must leave you now for ever.

Arline. Oh, no, no! say not so! I cannot live without you.

Thaddeus. And will you then forsake your home, your kindred, all! and follow me?

"Through the world wilt thou fly, love?"
Trio.

A. hush a fa-ther's sigh, love, That would heave for me;

T. Wilt fly from the world with me, wilt fly, fly, love, with

Devilshoof (coming down; to Thaddeus).

D. Come, come,

A. Through the world I would fly, From the world with

T. me? Come, my love, come, fly with

D. all the world hith-er fly, ____ Now, come a-way with

A. thee,

T. me, come, wilt thou For-tune's frowns de-fy, ____ love, as

D. me, ____ Nev-er let a lov-er's sigh ____ Ru-in

cresc.

★) These ten measures are sung on the stage without accompaniment.

(Thaddeus has barely time to take refuge in the cabinet, and Devilshoof to escape by the window, when the great doors are thrown open, and a brilliant assemblage enters, led by Count Arnheim, Florestein, etc. Count takes Arline's hand and presents her to the company.)

Count. Welcome, welcome all — share with me all the joy I feel while I present my loved and long-lost daughter.

Allegretto. **Finale.**

SOPRANO and ALTO.

dolce

Wel-come the pres-ent, oh pon-der not On the days de-part-ed now,—

TENOR.

dolce

Wel-come the pres-ent, oh pon-der not On the days de-part-ed now,—

BASS.

dolce

Chorus.

(A confused murmur is heard at the back of the stage.)

214

ear,   Check - ing young   joy's ca - reer?

ear,   Check - ing young   joy's ca - reer?

ear,   Check - ing young   joy's ca - reer?

cresc.   *f*

Queen (closely veiled, enters the apartment and goes up to Count Arnheim).

Heed the warn-ing   voice!__ Wail, and not re - joice!__ The

pp

foe to thy rest __ Is one thou lov'st best.__

(She lets her veil fall, and discovers the Queen of the Gipsies.)

Count. Recit.

Who, and what art thou? Let me know Whom dost thou deem my foe?

16118

Allegro.   Arline.

Count (rushing to the door of the cabinet;
Arline in vain opposes).

Thrown thus a-cross   thy

Stand not a-cross   my path!

Allegro.

path,   Let   me a-bide   thy wrath,   thy

Brave   not a fa - ther's wrath!   Brave   not a fa - ther's

(The Count pushes Arline aside, opens the door, and Thaddeus ap-

wrath!

wrath!

pears; the Count reels back, and every one seems panic-stricken.)

"Though ev'ry hope be fled."
Quintet and Chorus.

Andantino con moto. Thaddeus (to Arline).

Though ev - 'ry hope be fled, Which seem'd so

bright, which seem'd so bright be - fore, _____ The vengeance I would

scorn to dread, Which they on me _ can pour,

which they on me can pour, can

pour. Count (to Arline). Though

To shame and feel - ing dead, to feel - ing

218

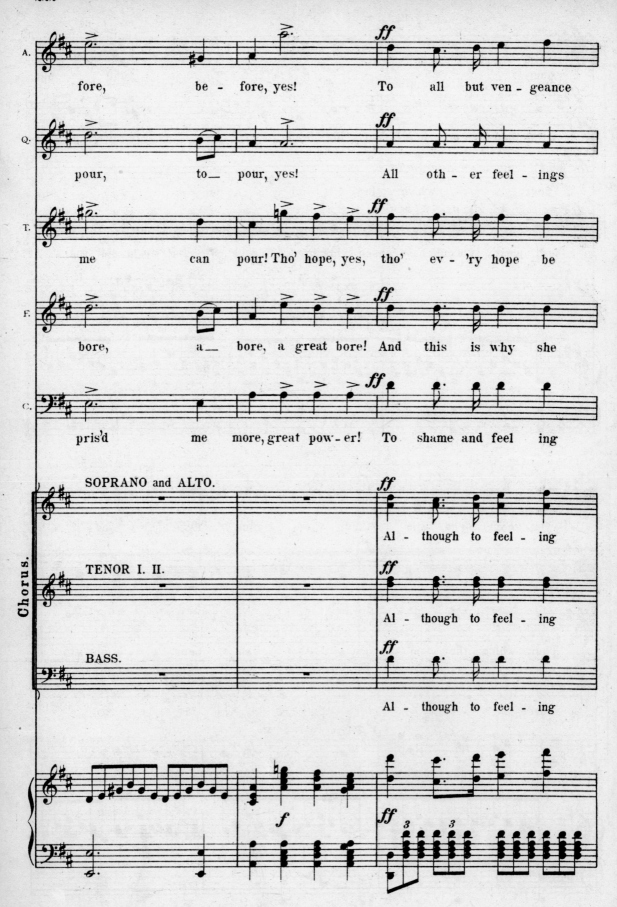

fore, be - fore, yes! To all but ven - geance

pour, to_ pour, yes! All oth - er feel - ings

me can pour! Tho' hope, yes, tho' ev - 'ry hope be

bore, a_ bore, a great bore! And this is why she

pris'd me more, great pow - er! To shame and feel ing

SOPRANO and ALTO.

Al - though to feel - ing

TENOR I. II.

Al - though to feel - ing

BASS.

Al - though to feel - ing

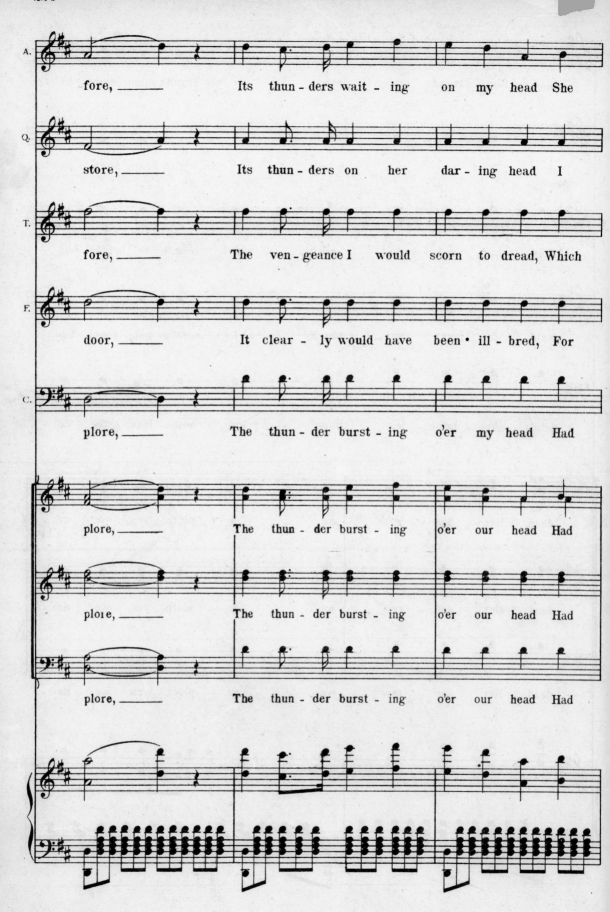

A. on - ly lives to_ pour, she on - ly

Q. on - ly live to pour, I on - ly

T. they on me can pour, which they on

F. ri - vals are a bore, for ri - vals

C. not surprised me more, had not sur-

not sur-prised us_ more, had not sur-

not sur-prised us_ more, had not sur-

not sur-prised us more, had not sur-

cre _

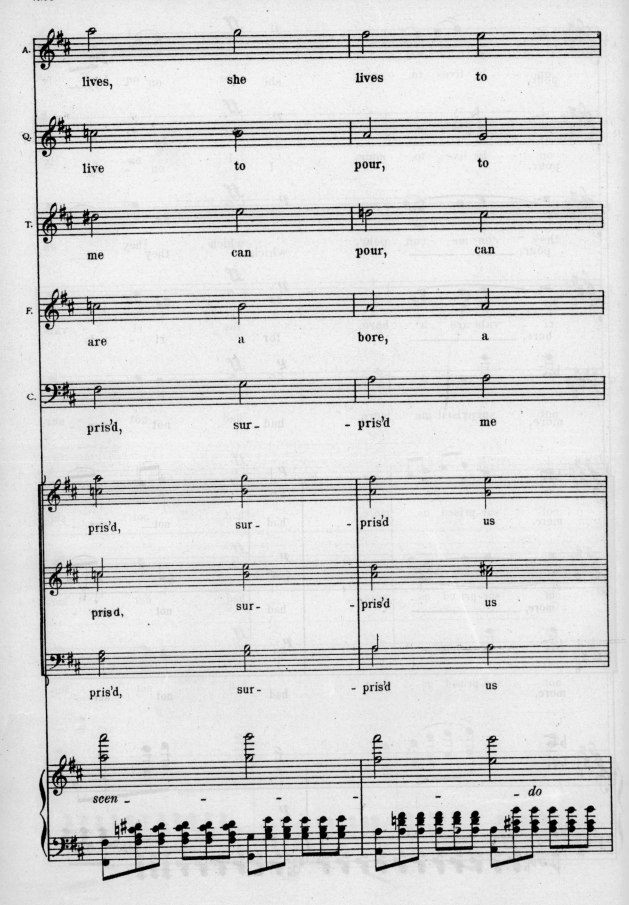

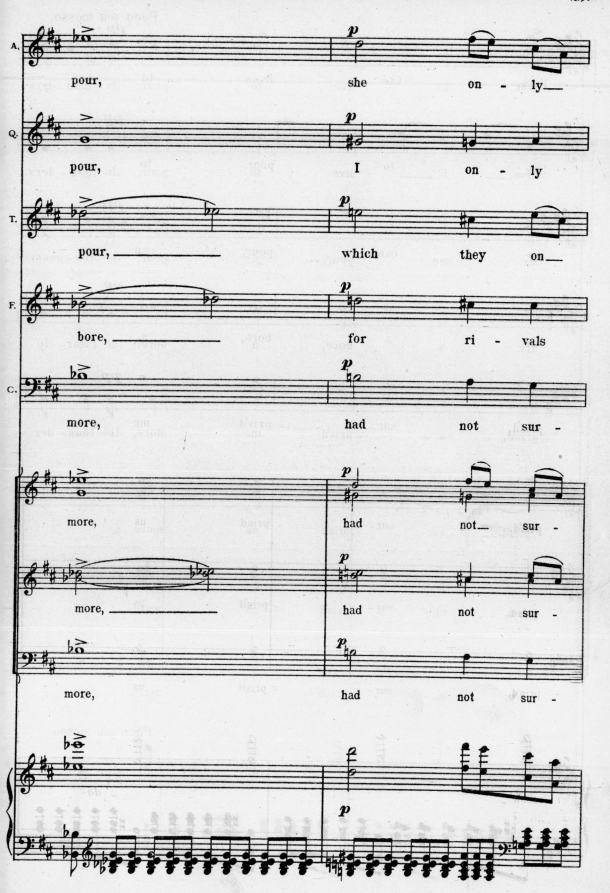

Poco più mosso.

A. lives, she lives to pour, its thun-ders

Q. live,___ I ___ live to pour, its thun-ders

T. me can pour, can pour, the ven-geance

F. are a bore, a bore! It clear-ly

C. pris'd, sur- -pris'd me more, the thun-der

pris'd,___ sur- -pris'd us more,

pris'd, sur- -pris'd us more,

pris'd, sur- -pris'd us more,

Poco più mosso.

head_ in all her hate to pour, in all her hate to pour, in

pour, its thunders on her dar - ing head I live to pour, I

scorn, which they on me can pour, which they on me can pour, which

bred, for ri - vals are a bore, yes, ri - vals are a bore, they

head, had not surpris'd, had not surpris'd, surpris'd me more, sur -

sur -

sur -

sur -

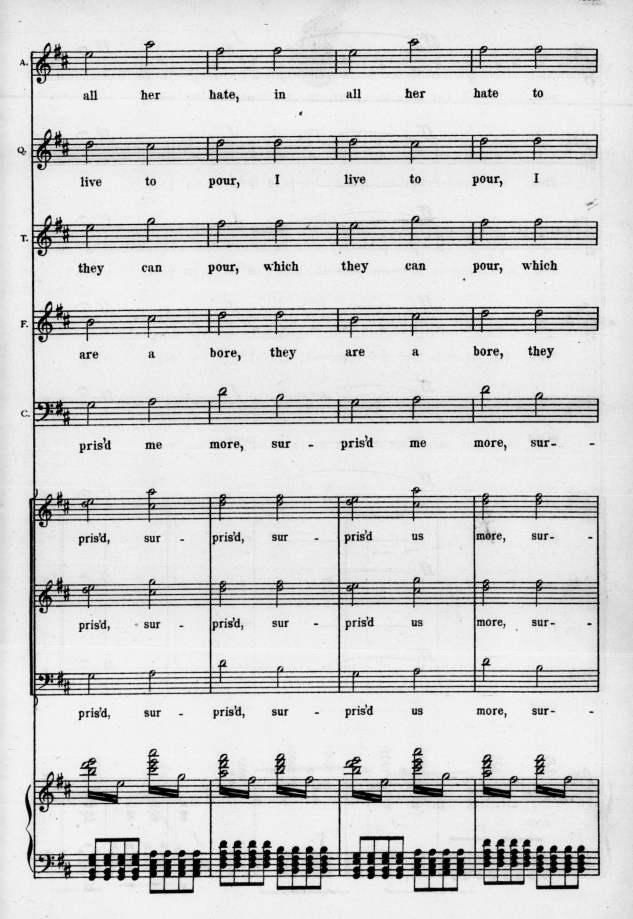

Allegro vivace.

Count (advancing to Thaddeus).

Leave the place thy pol-lut-ing step hath cross'd! De-part,
or thou art lost!

Thaddeus (casting a sorrowful look on Arline
as he is about to go).

To threats I should con-temn, For thy dear sake I yield.

Arline
(summoning resolution).

The burst-ing tor-rent I will stem, And him I live for,

(She takes Thaddeus by the hand and goes to the Count, then turns to the company.)

shield. Break not the on - ly tie, the on - ly

tie That bids my heart, my

heart re - joice, For

whom con - tent - ed I would die, — The

hus-band of my choice, the hus-band of my choice! De -

16118

(darting a furious look at Arline as she passes her)

Lento assai.

which enthrals thee!   Weep rivers! weep rivers! for a - ges

col canto

(As the Queen is dragging Thaddeus towards the
Arline (to the assembly).

pine! He shall nev-er, nev - er be thine!   Your par-don, if I

window, Arline stops him).

(Exeunt omnes at the large doors beside the win-

seek With my fa-ther a-lone to speak.   **Allegro.**

dows, which close upon them; the Queen is seen to pass out of the window.)

"See at your feet a suppliant."

Duettino.

238

16118

In a chain of such dis - grace? My rank, my ver-y blood de-fame,

With a blot no time can ef - face? The child of my heart,

of my house the pride, An out - cast, an out-cast Gip-sy's bride! The

child of my heart, of my house the pride, An out - cast Gip - sy's

Poco più mosso. **Thaddeus** (breaking from her, and going up with great dignity to the Count).

bride! Proud lord, al-tho' this head proscrib'd Should

fall by the weap - ons thy wealth hath brib'd, Al-tho' in re-veal-ing the

name I bear, The home I shall see no more, The

land which to thee, in its deep despair, The dead - liest ha - tred

bore:— I may fall, as have fall - en the brav - est of foes, the

"When the fair land of Poland."

Aria.

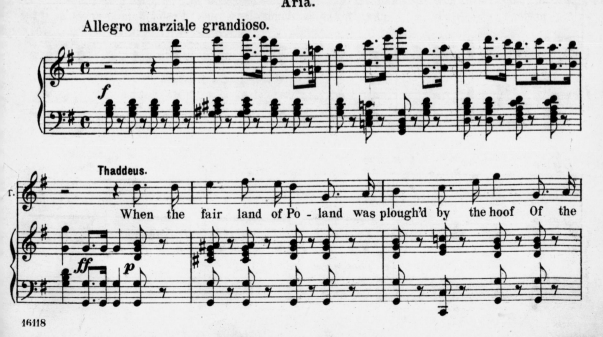

T. ruth-less in-vad-er, when Might, With steel to the bo-som, and

flame to the roof, Com-plet-ed her tri-umph o'er Right, In that

mo-ment of dan-ger, when Free-dom invok'd All the fet-ter-less sons of her

pride, In a pha-lanx as daunt-less as Free-dom e'er yok'd, I

fought and I bled by her side. My birth is no-ble, un-

poco meno mosso

stain'd my crest As is thine own: let this at-test! My

birth is no - ble, un-stain'd my crest As is thine own, as is thine own: let this at-

rall. *adagio assai*

col canto

test!

(Takes his commission, seen in Act I, from his bosom, and gives it to

ff *a tempo*

Larghetto cantabile.

the Count, who stands fixed and bewildered.)

p

f

rp

Thaddeus.

p e dolce

Pit - -y for one in child - hood torn From kin- -dred with whom she

dwelt, Rip- -en'd in af - ter - years to love, The

fond- -est that heart hath felt,— Has made me, thus far,

faith re-new With out - laws chance first link'd me to. As a

foe,— on this head let your ha - tred be pil'd, But de-

spise not one who hath so lov'd your child;— As a foe on this head let your

(Thaddeus, moved to tears, is about to fall at the Count's feet, who checks him.)

C. hold   Till the blood____ in its veins be cold!   Not at

C. mine:____ be that hom - age   paid at hers, Who the   firm - est af-fection on

C. thee confers,   who   the   firm - est af-fec-tion on   thee con-fers, who the

C. firm-est af-fec-tion on thee____ con - fers.

"Let not the heart."

Trio.

* In performing the Opera, these 8 measures are omitted, skipping to * at head of p. 250.

(During the trio, the wan figure of the Queen has been seen at the window in the back, and at the end of it, as Thaddeus is about to embrace Arline, the Queen, in a transport of rage, points him out to a Gipsy by her side, who is in the act of firing at him, when Devilshoof, who has tracked their steps, averts the Gipsy's aim, and by a rapid movement turns the musket towards the Queen—it goes off, and she falls.)

Count. Guard every portal—summon each guest and friend—
And this festive scene suspend.

(The distant sound of joyous instruments heard in the saloons, which the intelligence of the catastrophe is supposed to have reached, ceases, and crowds of nobles, ladies, guests, etc., pour in at each door.)

Allegro pesante.

"Oh, what full delight."
Final Aria.

(Arline rushes into the arms of Thaddeus, and then passes over to the Count.)

Oh, what full de - light thro' my bo - som thrills,

And a wild-er glow in my heart in - stils!

Oh, what full de - light Thro' my bo - som thrills,

And a wild-er glow my heart in- -stils!

Bliss un-felt, un - felt be-fore, Hope with-out, with - out al -loy,

Speak with rap - tur'd, rap-tur'd tone, Of my heart the—

End of the Opera.